# MATHS
## OFFICIAL WORKBOOK
### AGES 7-8

DAN LIPSCOMBE
AND LEISA BOVEY

# INTRODUCTION

## HOW TO USE THIS BOOK

Welcome to an exciting educational experience! Your child will go on a series of adventures through the amazing world of Minecraft, improving their maths skills along the way. Matched to the National Curriculum for maths for ages 7–8 (Year 3), this workbook takes your child into fascinating landscapes where our heroes Oscar and Maya embark on building projects and daring treasure hunts…all while keeping those pesky mobs at bay!

As each adventure unfolds, your child will complete topic-based questions worth a certain number of emeralds . These can then be 'traded in' on the final page. The more challenging questions are marked with this icon  to stretch your child's learning. Answers are included at the back of the book.

## MEET OUR HEROES

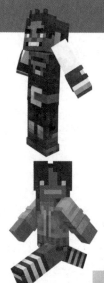

Oscar is very athletic. Not many people can keep up with him when he is exploring. He never seems to stand still! He is forever running, jumping and swimming – eager to reach something new and exciting. Sometimes he is so active that he forgets to eat. Oscar quite likes Endermen because they are also fast but, if he has to fight one, you can count on him!

Maya can be quite shy. She likes to spend time in her own company, often with a good book. She enjoys building and discovering new materials. Her favourite block is quartz. Don't let her quiet personality fool you, though. Maya is very handy with a bow and arrow and fights never scare her. She is smart and will retreat to home if she knows the fight can't be won.

First published in 2021 by Collins
An imprint of HarperCollinsPublishers
1 London Bridge Street, London, SE1 9GF

HarperCollinsPublishers
1st Floor, Watermarque Building, Ringsend Road, Dublin 4, Ireland

Publisher: Fiona McGlade
Authors: Dan Lipscombe and Leisa Bovey
Project management: Richard Toms
Design: Ian Wrigley and Sarah Duxbury
Typesetting: Nicola Lancashire at Rose and Thorn Creative Services

Special thanks to Alex Wiltshire, Sherin Kwan and Marie-Louise Bengtsson at Mojang and the team at Farshore

Production: Karen Nulty

ISBN: 978-0-00-846276-5

British Library Cataloguing in Publication Data.

A CIP record of this book is available from the British Library.

1 2 3 4 5 6 7 8 9 10

Printed in the United Kingdom

MIX
Paper from responsible source
FSC
www.fsc.org
FSC™ C007454

This book is produced from independently certified FSC™ paper to ensure responsible forest management.

For more information visit: www.harpercollins.co.uk/green

# CONTENTS

::::::::::::::::::::::::::::::::::::::::::::::

# NUMBER AND PLACE VALUE

## SETTING THE SCENE

In the huge expanse of the plains biome, oak trees stretch among tall grasses. Chickens peck away at grass, looking for seeds. Cows and sheep graze the greenery, while pigs snuffle around in between. Occasionally a bee can be spotted dancing from flower to flower, collecting pollen to take home to its hive, where it will make honey.

## RIVERS FULL OF LIFE

There aren't many hills in the plains. It's a rather flat place, which dips here and there towards a winding river full of salmon...or the occasional hostile mob. In these rivers you might find the drowned, a zombie which spends its life trudging through the waters.

## BASE CAMP

It's in the plains that many adventurers set up home. With plenty of wood and food, it's an area suited to building a house and creating a farm. Much like our two adventure-seeking heroes.

## JOBS TO DO

Oscar has done so much harvesting and crafting that the storage chests are a mess. It's time to do some organising. Oscar waves goodbye to Maya as he heads out of the house and across to the storage shed.

# PLACE VALUE

Oscar has a big job ahead of him. There are so many chests in the storage room and each of them has hundreds of items and crafting materials. He decides the best thing to do is split everything into organised stacks.

**1**

Oscar starts with the cobblestone. There's a lot here. He breaks down the stacks into piles of 50. Two of these equal 100. Help Oscar complete this number pattern.

200     300     ☐     ☐     600     ☐     800

**2**

Partition each number into hundreds, tens and ones.

a)  372 = ☐ + ☐ + ☐         b)  236 = ☐ + ☐ + ☐

c)  645 = ☐ + ☐ + ☐         d)  890 = ☐ + ☐ + ☐

**3**

Oscar has learned a lot about numbers and knows that they can be broken down in different ways.

For example:     326 = 300 + 20 + 6

326 = 320 + 6

326 = 310 + 16

Write down two different ways each of these numbers can be broken down.

a)  576   ...................................................   ...................................................

b)  873   ...................................................   ...................................................

c)  987   ...................................................   ...................................................

# REPRESENTING NUMBERS

Oscar opens a chest and finds lots of pumpkins. In order to visualise how many there are, he imagines them in groups.

## 1

What numbers are represented here?

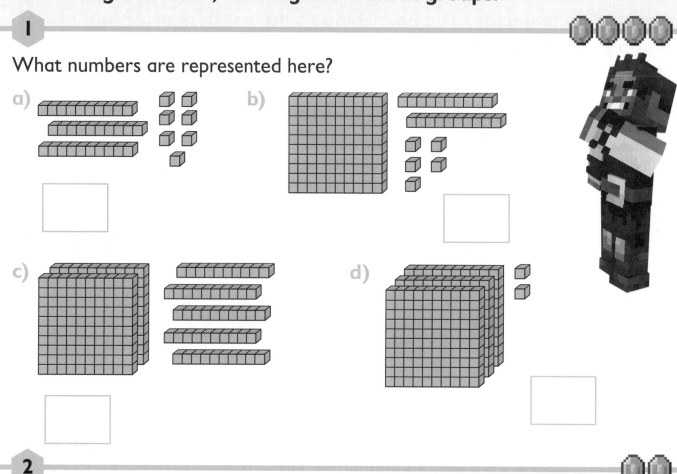

a)

b)

c)

d)

## 2

Complete the place value charts to show the three-digit numbers given below.

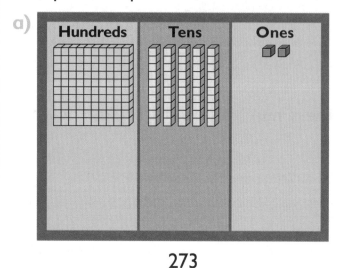

a)

| Hundreds | Tens | Ones |
|---|---|---|

273

b)

| Hundreds | Tens | Ones |
|---|---|---|
| (100) (100) (100) | (10) (10) | I I I |

458

Oscar moves onto a chest which contains only coal. The fuel is scattered in different sized stacks. He decides to fill his inventory.

**3**

Using these given values, write the number represented by each row.

= 100      = 10      = 1

a)

b)

**4**

What numbers are the arrows pointing to on the number lines?

a)        b)        c)

100                                                                200

d)    e)                          f)

600                                                                700

**5**

Estimate the number each arrow is pointing to.

a)    b)                          c)

0                                                                100

COLOUR IN HOW MANY
EMERALDS YOU EARNED

# READING AND WRITING NUMBERS

**Oscar decides to create a new building for smelting and cooking, featuring signs made from leftover wood.**

**1**

Help Oscar with the signs by writing these numbers in digits.

a)  Sixty-five

b)  Three hundred and sixteen

**2**

Write these numbers in words.

a)  379 ...............................................................................................

b)  783 ...............................................................................................

**3**

Write the amount of iron Oscar has in both digits and words.

 = 100     = 10     = 1

a)

Digits: ☐    Words: ...............................................................

b)

Digits: ☐    Words: ...............................................................

Oscar browses through everything he and Maya have collected. He notices some books which haven't been crafted into bookcases. Each book features a number on the cover.

**4**

Write the largest three-digit number that can be made from each set of book covers in both digits and words.

a)  Digits:

Words: ......................................................................

b)  Digits:

Words: ......................................................................

c)  Digits:

Words: ......................................................................

**5**

Write the smallest three-digit number that can be made from each set of music discs in both digits and words.

a)  Digits:

Words: ......................................................................

b)  Digits:

Words: ......................................................................

c)  Digits:

Words: ......................................................................

# 10 AND 100 MORE OR LESS

Oscar has constructed a few extra buildings to make his and Maya's home more of a mini village. He wants to make a map of their base but needs help to work out the distances between the buildings.

**1**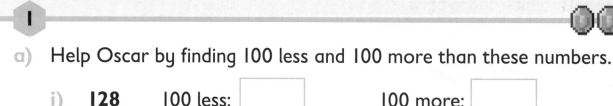

a) Help Oscar by finding 100 less and 100 more than these numbers.

i) **128**    100 less: ☐    100 more: ☐

ii) **687**    100 less: ☐    100 more: ☐

b) Help him to find 10 less and 10 more than these numbers.

i) **317**    10 less: ☐    10 more: ☐

ii) **409**    10 less: ☐    10 more: ☐

**2**

Complete this place value table by drawing the pictures and writing the numbers in digits on the answer lines.

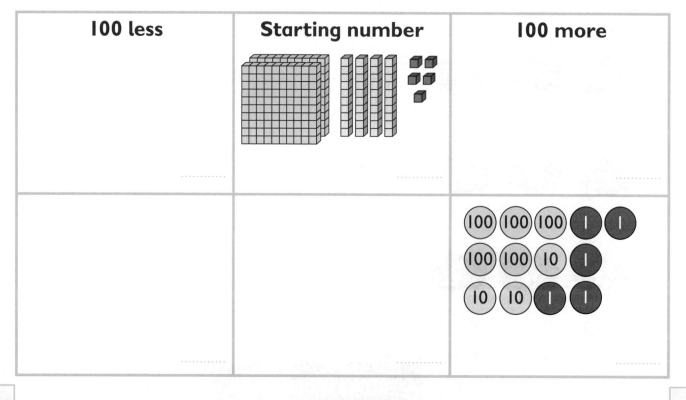

| 100 less | Starting number | 100 more |
|---|---|---|

**3**

Complete the table by drawing the pictures and writing the missing numbers in digits.

| 10 less | Starting number | 10 more |
|---|---|---|
| ............. | ............. | ............. |
| ............. | ............. | ............. |

**4**

Decide whether these statements are always true, sometimes true, or never true when starting with a three-digit number.

a) The tens column changes when you add or subtract 10.

Always ☐   Sometimes ☐   Never ☐

b) The hundreds column changes when you add or subtract 10.

Always ☐   Sometimes ☐   Never ☐

c) The ones column changes when you add or subtract 10.

Always ☐   Sometimes ☐   Never ☐

d) More than one column changes when you add or subtract 10.

Always ☐   Sometimes ☐   Never ☐

COLOUR IN HOW MANY
EMERALDS YOU EARNED

# COUNTING IN MULTIPLES

**While Oscar is tidying, he finds some fireworks he made ages ago. He sets up a dispenser to launch the fireworks once a lever is pulled. The lever is connected to the dispenser by a trail of redstone dust.**

**1**

Use multiples of 4, 8, 50 and 100 to complete the missing stages of these fireworks before blasting off.

a)

| 24 |
|----|
| 20 |
|    |
|    |
| 8  |
| 4  |

b)

| 48 |
|----|
|    |
| 32 |
|    |
|    |
| 8  |

c)

|     |
|-----|
| 250 |
| 200 |
|     |
|     |
| 50  |

d)

|     |
|-----|
| 500 |
|     |
|     |
|     |
| 100 |

**2**

Look at these signs above the levers.

Find the largest number that each row shows multiples of.

a)     Multiples of ⬜

b)  Multiples of ⬜

c)   Multiples of ⬜

Redstone dust carries a signal that can power special blocks, like pistons. Oscar is practising using it. He starts by placing redstone torches and a piston. Can you help to join the items with redstone?

**3**

Colour two circuits across this grid. One circuit is going up in multiples of 4 and the other in multiples of 8.

You can connect the numbers diagonally or in straight lines.

Draw a torch at the start of each circuit and a piston at the end.

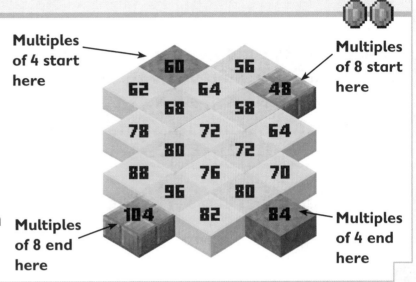

Multiples of 4 start here

Multiples of 8 start here

Multiples of 8 end here

Multiples of 4 end here

Grid numbers: 60, 56, 62, 64, 48, 68, 58, 78, 72, 64, 80, 72, 88, 76, 70, 96, 80, 104, 82, 84

**4**

These circuits make number patterns. Fill in the gaps.

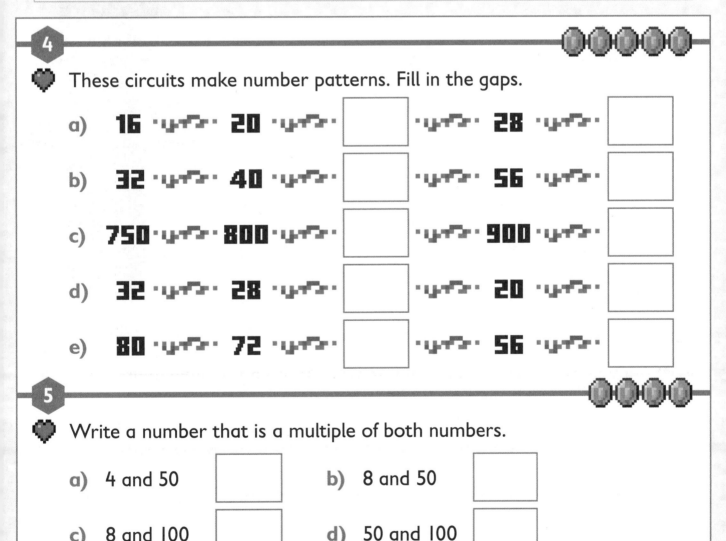

a) **16** → **20** → ☐ → **28** → ☐

b) **32** → **40** → ☐ → **56** → ☐

c) **750** → **800** → ☐ → **900** → ☐

d) **32** → **28** → ☐ → **20** → ☐

e) **80** → **72** → ☐ → **56** → ☐

**5**

Write a number that is a multiple of both numbers.

a) 4 and 50 ☐

b) 8 and 50 ☐

c) 8 and 100 ☐

d) 50 and 100 ☐

# COMPARING AND ORDERING NUMBERS

Oscar wants to lay minecart tracks to connect the house to a deep mining system they've been digging out. He needs a good understanding of numbers to compare the different amounts of wood, iron, gold and redstone dust required.

 **1**

Write these values in order of size from smallest to largest.

a)   146, 130, 115, 122, 101

.......................................................................................

b)   277, 275, 263, 226, 252

.......................................................................................

c)   69, 36, 46, 57, 48

.......................................................................................

d)   370, 366, 368, 379, 374

.......................................................................................

**2**

Write any number that could come between these pairs of numbers.

a)   56 and 64

b)   128 and 134

c)   375 and 382

d)   412 and 433

Oscar begins to place the tracks and craft some minecarts with chests. The sun is starting to set and mobs will be out soon. Help him to get a move on with some more calculations he needs to do.

**3**

Fill in the boxes with **>**, **<** or **=** to make each statement correct.

a)  872 ☐ 902

b)  734 ☐ 724

c)  621 ☐ 600 + 20 + 1

d)  736 ☐ 800 + 70 + 9

**4**

Make six different three-digit numbers using the minecarts. Then order them from smallest to largest.

**5**

♥ Complete parts a) to c) with suitable numbers. Complete d) with a symbol.

a)  983 > 900 + ☐ + 3

b)  2 hundreds and 8 tens < 2 ☐ 5

c)  200 + ☐ + 7 = 100 + ☐ + 80 + 7

d)  3 hundreds and four ones ☐ 3 hundreds and four tens

# NUMBER PROBLEMS

**Maya has asked for some andesite for building, so Oscar sends up a chest by pressing a button to turn on the powered minecart track.**

### 1

Here are four chest minecarts filled with andesite:

A **432**   B **384**   C **289**   D **347**

Maya removes 10 blocks from minecart A and places them in minecart B. She removes 100 blocks from minecart C and places them in minecart D.

a) Write down the amount of andesite in each minecart now.

Cart A: ☐   Cart B: ☐   Cart C: ☐   Cart D: ☐

b) Order the new amounts of andesite in the minecarts from smallest to largest.

.........................................................................

### 2

Oscar thinks of a number. He subtracts 10, then adds 100, and adds 3. His answer is 379.

What number did Oscar think of? ☐

### 3

Fill in the missing numbers in this grid. Start at the top left.

Each column increases in equal steps.

Each row increases in equal steps too.

| 12 | | | | |
|----|----|----|----|----|
| | | | | |
| 20 | | | | |
| | 32 | | | |
| | | 50 | 150 | |
| | | | 300 | |
| | | | | 500 |

**COLOUR IN HOW MANY EMERALDS YOU EARNED**

# ADVENTURE ROUND-UP

## CREEPER ON THE TRACKS

Oscar hops into a minecart and rides it home. He's achieved a lot today. As the minecart rattles along the tracks, Oscar hears a BOOM! A creeper must have been waiting ahead and spotted him on the way home. The explosion destroys a small section of the tracks. As Oscar jumps out to repair the tracks, he's swarmed by zombies and skeletons which creep out from the darkness.

## ARROWS FLY

Oscar swings his sword wildly, chopping left and right, fighting back against the mobs. But they keep coming. In the dusk a light appears close to the ground. Into this bright spot steps Maya with a bow drawn back. Arrows begin to fly, picking off the mobs still reaching out for Oscar. Together they keep battling until morning comes and the mobs stop spawning.

# ADDITION AND SUBTRACTION

## SANDY LAND

The badlands biome is made up of red sand and terracotta. Adventurers will see shades of red and brown terracotta, which can be easily harvested with a pickaxe and used to decorate and build. The sand is littered with dead plant life, dried out from the heat and lack of water.

## GOING FOR GOLD

Hunters of precious metals can strike it rich in the badlands. Abandoned mineshafts are bursting with gold ore just waiting to be recovered.

## BRIGHT AND BEAUTIFUL

Explorers may see a shambling husk stuck in the bright daylight or encounter mobs at night. There's no easy access to food, but it's a beautiful place to explore.

### BOUND FOR THE BADLANDS

Maya had seen a new biome while out exploring recently. From a distance, she saw layers of colourful rock with tall mountain peaks. It must be the badlands! She packs a set of tools and plenty of food and goes off to search for excitement.

# ADDING AND SUBTRACTING MENTALLY

**Maya is walking towards the badlands. She's enjoying the scenery and the sunshine.**

**1**

Use partitioning to do these additions mentally.

Example: 89 + 53 = (80 + 50) + (9 + 3)

$$= \quad 130 \quad + \quad 12 \quad = \quad 142$$

a) 14 + 85 = (........ + ........) + (........ + ........)

= ........ + ........ = ........

b) 484 + 502 = (........ + ........) + (........ + ........) + (........ + ........)

= ........ + ........ + ........ = ........

**2**

Work out these subtractions by counting up from the smaller to the larger number to find the difference.

Example:

85 − 17 = | 68 |

+ 3     + 60     + 5

17   20        80   85

a) 53 − 14 = [ ]

14   20        50   53

b) 94 − 48 = [ ]

48   50        90   94

 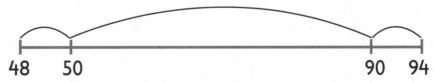

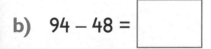
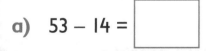

# ADDING IN COLUMNS

Before Maya begins exploring, she sets up a small camp. She plans to return here to sleep if things get too dangerous. She uses some wooden planks from home to build a shelter and places a spare bed, along with some torches and a crafting table. The first thing to harvest is all this colourful terracotta for building. Help her to figure out how many blocks she needs.

 **1**

Complete these column additions with two-digit numbers.

a)
```
    7 3
 +  1 6
 _____


 _____
```

b)
```
    4 2
 +  5 3
 _____


 _____
```

c)
```
    3 7
 +  7 1
 _____


 _____
```

d)
```
    2 2
 +  3 6
 _____


 _____
```

**2**

Complete these column additions with three-digit numbers.

a)
```
   2 1 3
 + 7 1 5
 _____


 _____
```

b)
```
   7 6 3
 + 1 3 4
 _____


 _____
```

c)
```
   2 4 3
 + 6 5 6
 _____


 _____
```

d)
```
   4 1 8
 + 3 0 1
 _____


 _____
```

Maya is working her way through layers of terracotta. As she digs, she hears a strange noise, which sounds like an echoing howl. This means there's a cave system very close by. Answer these questions to help her obtain all the terracotta she needs.

**3**

Complete these column additions with two-digit numbers and exchanges.

a)
```
    5 8
+   2 6
_____

_____
```

b)
```
    1 7
+   7 8
_____

_____
```

c)
```
    6 2
+   8 3
_____

_____
```

d)
```
    5 4
+   6 3
_____

_____
```

e)
```
    2 8
+   8 6
_____

_____
```

f)
```
    4 9
+   9 2
_____

_____
```

**4**

Complete these column additions with three-digit numbers and exchanges.

a)
```
    6 6 3
+   1 2 9
_____

_____
```

b)
```
    5 6 9
+   3 0 7
_____

_____
```

c)
```
    7 2 1
+   1 3 9
_____

_____
```

d)
```
    1 7 6
+   4 3 2
_____

_____
```

e)
```
    3 2 8
+   2 8 3
_____

_____
```

f)
```
    8 0 8
+   1 7 3
_____

_____
```

**5**

Fill in the missing digits in these column additions.

a)
```
    4 ☐ 8
+   ☐ 1 1
_____
    6 5 9
```

b)
```
    ☐ 3 2
+   2 5 ☐
_____
    7 9 1
```

c)
```
    ☐ 2 7
+   4 3 ☐
_____
    7 6 4
```

d)
```
    6 ☐ 7
+   2 9 ☐
_____
    9 0 5
```

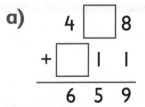

**COLOUR IN HOW MANY EMERALDS YOU EARNED**

21

# SUBTRACTING IN COLUMNS

The next day, Maya heads off into the valleys of the badlands. Before she gets too far, she sees a few husks roaming about. They soon take notice of her, and she prepares to fight them. Maya swings her sword powerfully in battle and the husks gradually see their health decrease.

**1**

Complete these column subtractions with two-digit numbers.

a)
```
   9 9
 − 1 5
 _____

 _____
```

b)
```
   7 8
 − 3 6
 _____

 _____
```

c)
```
   8 8
 − 3 2
 _____

 _____
```

d)
```
   5 3
 − 1 2
 _____

 _____
```

**2**

Complete these column subtractions with three-digit numbers.

a)
```
   6 7 6
 − 2 4 2
 _____

 _____
```

b)
```
   7 3 4
 − 6 2 1
 _____

 _____
```

c)
```
   8 6 3
 − 7 1 2
 _____

 _____
```

d)
```
   2 4 9
 − 1 0 8
 _____

 _____
```

With the husks defeated, Maya carries on her exploration. While looking for openings in the ground that may lead to caves, she continues to calculate how many more blocks she needs to mine.

**3**

Complete these column subtractions with two-digit numbers and exchanges.

a)
```
    6 2
 -  2 7
 _____

 _____
```

b)
```
    9 3
 -  1 6
 _____

 _____
```

c)
```
    4 6
 -  2 8
 _____

 _____
```

d)
```
    7 3
 -  3 8
 _____

 _____
```

e)
```
    9 4
 -  7 9
 _____

 _____
```

f)
```
    5 5
 -  1 7
 _____

 _____
```

**4**

Complete these column subtractions with three-digit numbers and exchanges.

a)
```
    8 5 2
 -  2 1 8
 _____

 _____
```

b)
```
    4 7 2
 -  2 6 6
 _____

 _____
```

c)
```
    5 0 5
 -  3 2 4
 _____

 _____
```

d)
```
    7 1 8
 -  3 8 0
 _____

 _____
```

e)
```
    1 3 1
 -  1 1 9
 _____

 _____
```

f)
```
    9 2 8
 -  8 3 6
 _____

 _____
```

Maya takes a certain number of steps to the north. On the last step, she looks down and finds the opening of a very deep cave!

**5**

 Fill in the missing digits in these column subtractions.

a)
```
    5 □
 -  □ 4
 _____
    1 1
```

b)
```
    □ 4
 -  4 □
 _____
    4 2
```

c)
```
    6 □ 4
 -  2 3 □
 _____
    4 0 4
```

d)
```
    5 □ 9
 -  2 4 □
 _____
    3 3 7
```

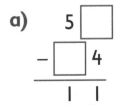

COLOUR IN HOW MANY
EMERALDS YOU EARNED

23

# ESTIMATING AND CHECKING

As Maya peers into the mouth of the cave, she tries to estimate how far down it goes. Answer these problems to help with her estimations.

**1**

Circle the number you estimate to be closest to the real answer.

a) **21 × 5 =**          100      10      1,000

b) **100 ÷ 24 =**        40       4       400

c) **478 + 296 =**       780      78      7,800

d) **711 − 660 =**       5        50      500

**2**

Circle the most sensible estimate for each calculation.

a) **315 + 216 =**       300 + 200 = 500          350 + 250 = 600

b) **660 − 564 =**       660 − 560 = 100          700 − 550 = 150

c) **58 ÷ 5 =**          50 ÷ 5 = 10              60 ÷ 5 = 12

d) **12 × 8 =**          12 × 10 = 120            12 × 5 = 60

Maya finds an abandoned mineshaft. It doesn't go very far, but there is a minecart with a chest. Someone has left a lot of gold ore!

**3**

The label on each minecart chest shows how much gold ore it holds when full. Estimate the number of gold ore blocks in the minecart chests.

a)    Holds 40, about half full

b)    Holds 150, about $\frac{1}{3}$ full

c)    Holds 100, about $\frac{3}{4}$ full

Maya is finding all kinds of valuable materials in the badlands – gold ore in the mineshaft, some lapis lazuli in the surface walls and even a handful of diamonds near a pool of lava. Below you can see some of the items she has found and calculations for them.

 **4**

Write an inverse calculation you can use to check if the answer is correct.

a)  58 + 63 = 121 ............................................

b) 257 – 129 = 128 ............................................

c) 150 ÷ 10 = 15 ............................................

d)  14 × 2 = 28 ............................................

**5**

First, write down an estimate for each of these calculations. Then calculate the exact answer. Finally, check your answer using an inverse calculation.

a)
```
  4 3 3
+ 5 6 5
-------

-------
```

b)
```
  6 7 6
- 2 3 4
-------

-------
```

Estimate: ..............................   Estimate: ..............................

Calculated answer: ☐   Calculated answer: ☐

Check:   Check:

# WORD PROBLEMS

**Maya leaves the cave behind. She breaks down her temporary shelter and heads for home. Waiting at home is Oscar.**

 **1**

Maya has 297 points of experience and Oscar has 387 points of experience.

Oscar says: "I have 100 more points than you."

Is Oscar correct? Explain your answer.

....................................................................................................................

**2**

First, write down an estimate for each of these calculations. Then calculate the exact answer. Finally, check your answer using an inverse calculation.

**a)** There are three chests. The first chest has 361 gold ore. The second chest has 98 more gold ore than the first. The third chest has 112 coal.

How many items are there altogether in the three chests?

Estimate: ...........................................

Calculated answer: ☐

Check:

**b)** Maya needs 192 wheat from the farm to make bread. She has gathered 100, 11 and 8 wheat so far.

How many more wheat does Maya need to find?

Estimate: ...........................................

Calculated answer: ☐

Check:

**COLOUR IN HOW MANY EMERALDS YOU EARNED** ◇◇◇◇◇◇◇

# ADVENTURE ROUND-UP

## LOTS OF RESOURCES

Maya tells Oscar all about the beautiful badlands. She shows him the building materials she collected, as well as the iron, gold and diamonds she mined. Together, they separate everything into chests.

## TOUGHER TESTS

As Maya and Oscar talk late into the night, they decide that very soon they will need to begin preparing to take on tougher enemies. In order to do this, they need stronger weapons and tougher armour. They also need to learn how to enchant their tools and craft helpful potions.

## DREAMING OF THE NETHER

Tomorrow, Oscar will head off to explore the snowy forests of a taiga biome, hoping to find some wolves which will fight by their sides. He also needs to collect lava and water, in order to create obsidian. They will use obsidian to build a Nether portal, which can transport them to another dimension – the Nether!

# MULTIPLICATION AND DIVISION

## A SNOWY SIGHT

The bright greens fade to a darker shade in the snowy taiga biome. Long grasses are replaced by small ferns and the trees here are spruce. Snow extends as far as the eye can see, only melting around the bases of some trees. Owing to the cold air, there are hardly any flowers, but berry bushes sprout here and there.

## CREATURES OF THE COLD

The only animals to be found have to cope with the cold. Foxes curl up as balls of white fluff and are easily spooked when approached. However, wolves roam freely and stare at any humans who enter the snowy taiga.

## FROZEN UNDER FOOT

While rivers do cross the land, much of the water has frozen to ice, which can be walked on. The ice isn't easily harvested. However, the snow can be gathered with a shovel, leading to the odd snowball fight.

## TAIGA TASKS

Oscar left home early this morning to enter the snowy taiga. He has only a few tasks on his list for today and he hopes to develop a plan for entering the Nether while out in the peace of this white wonderland.

# MULTIPLICATION AND DIVISION FACTS

The grass around Oscar is now covered with snow that crunches underfoot. From where he has entered the snowy taiga, he can see a few berry bushes and a fox curled up under a tree canopy. Oscar creeps slowly past the fox to harvest some berries.

**1**

Write two multiplication facts and two division facts for each array.

a)

$$\boxed{\phantom{0}} \times \boxed{\phantom{0}} = \boxed{\phantom{0}}$$

$$\boxed{\phantom{0}} \times \boxed{\phantom{0}} = \boxed{\phantom{0}}$$

$$\boxed{\phantom{0}} \div \boxed{\phantom{0}} = \boxed{\phantom{0}}$$

$$\boxed{\phantom{0}} \div \boxed{\phantom{0}} = \boxed{\phantom{0}}$$

b)

$$\boxed{\phantom{0}} \times \boxed{\phantom{0}} = \boxed{\phantom{0}} \qquad \boxed{\phantom{0}} \div \boxed{\phantom{0}} = \boxed{\phantom{0}}$$

$$\boxed{\phantom{0}} \times \boxed{\phantom{0}} = \boxed{\phantom{0}} \qquad \boxed{\phantom{0}} \div \boxed{\phantom{0}} = \boxed{\phantom{0}}$$

**2**

Use the multiplication and division facts you know to help solve these.

a) $320 \div 4 = \boxed{\phantom{0}}$

b) $40 \times \boxed{\phantom{0}} = 320$

c) $3 \times 70 = \boxed{\phantom{0}}$

d) $210 \div 30 = \boxed{\phantom{0}}$

# DOUBLING AND HALVING

Oscar is happily chopping down some trees for the extra wood. As he clears a particularly tall tree, behind it he finds a small grey face looking at him. The wolf pup whines a little and Oscar looks around to see if any grown-up wolves are nearby, but he doesn't find any.

**1**

Draw lines to join each number to its double.

 12

 50

 60

 70

 120

 16

 8

 35

 40

 25

 24

 20

**2**

Do some more doubling to help Oscar. The input number is the number that is doubled and the output is the result. Fill in these missing input and output numbers.

a) Input: 24     Output:

b) Input:     Output: 14

c) Input: 45     Output:

d) Input:     Output: 140

**Oscar feeds the wolf pup a few bones from his pocket. The wolf nuzzles close to him. It seems that they've become friends. Oscar calls the wolf Moon and it trots alongside him.**

**3**

Write the missing numbers in words to complete these sentences.

a)  Half of 30 spruce logs is ........................................................ spruce logs.

b)  Double ................................................ chickens is 18 chickens.

c)  Half of ................................................ ferns is 44 ferns.

d)  Double ................................................ snowballs is 80 snowballs.

**4**

Fill in the boxes to complete these calculations.

a)  ☐ × 2 = 16          ☐ × 4 = 16          ☐ × 8 = 16

b)  ☐ × 2 = 24          ☐ × 4 = 24          ☐ × 8 = 24

c)  ☐ × 2 = 32          ☐ × 4 = 32          ☐ × 8 = 32

d)  ☐ × 2 = 40          ☐ × 4 = 40          ☐ × 8 = 40

**5**

♥ Fill in the boxes to complete each set of calculations.

a)  25 × 2 = 50          25 × 4 = ☐          25 × 8 = ☐

b)  5 × 4 = 20          5 × 8 = ☐          5 × 16 = ☐

**COLOUR IN HOW MANY EMERALDS YOU EARNED**

# 3 AND 4 TIMES TABLES

Now Oscar has a happy little wolf pup with him, he needs to find some meat to feed it. Oscar only brought bread for himself to snack on, so he needs to do some hunting. He saw some chickens at the edge of the snowy taiga. As well as raw chicken, they drop feathers when defeated.

**1**

Fill in the multiplication grid.

| | ×1 | ×2 | ×3 | ×4 | ×5 | ×6 | ×7 | ×8 | ×9 | ×10 | ×11 | ×12 |
|---|---|---|---|---|---|---|---|---|---|---|---|---|
| 3 | | | | | | | | | | | | |
| 4 | | | | | | | | | | | | |

**2**

Here are some sets of feathers. Write down the times tables facts you can use to find the total number of feathers.

a)

[ ] × [ ] = [ ]

[ ] × [ ] = [ ]

b)

[ ] × [ ] = [ ]

[ ] × [ ] = [ ]

c)

[ ] × [ ] = [ ]

[ ] × [ ] = [ ]

d)

[ ] × [ ] = [ ]

[ ] × [ ] = [ ]

After hunting the chickens, Oscar has plenty of food for Moon. Plus, he has feathers to make arrows when he gets home. Oscar sets up a campfire and organises his inventory while the wolf pup watches on.

 **3**

Oscar needs to split these items into equal groups. Write and answer the calculation to divide each set of items into equal groups.

a) Divide 32 feathers into 4 equal groups: ☐ ÷ ☐ = ☐

b) Divide 12 raw chickens into 3 equal groups: ☐ ÷ ☐ = ☐

c) Divide 36 berries into 12 equal groups: ☐ ÷ ☐ = ☐

**4**

Work these out.

a) Leather tunics cost 4 emeralds each. How many emeralds would it cost to buy 7 leather tunics? ☐

b) A villager has 24 emeralds. How many cooked chicken costing 3 emeralds each can they buy? ☐

c) Another villager has 36 emeralds. How many leather tunics costing 4 emeralds each can they buy? ☐

**5**

♥ Write down all the multiplication and division facts that this image shows.

☐ × ☐ = ☐     ☐ × ☐ = ☐

☐ ÷ ☐ = ☐     ☐ ÷ ☐ = ☐

**COLOUR IN HOW MANY EMERALDS YOU EARNED**

# 8 TIMES TABLE

Oscar has plenty of wood stored up now. He shouldn't need any more for a long time. Instead of chopping down more trees, Oscar decides to explore further and see what catches his eye.

**1**

Fill in the multiplication grid.

|  | ×1 | ×2 | ×3 | ×4 | ×5 | ×6 | ×7 | ×8 | ×9 | ×10 | ×11 | ×12 |
|---|---|---|---|---|---|---|---|---|---|---|---|---|
|  8 |  |  |  |  |  |  |  |  |  |  |  |  |

**2**

You can use a bar model to show multiplication and division. For example, this bar model shows 8 × 7 = 56, 7 × 8 = 56, 56 ÷ 8 = 7 and 56 ÷ 7 = 8.

| 56 | | | | | | |
|---|---|---|---|---|---|---|
| 8 | 8 | 8 | 8 | 8 | 8 | 8 |

Draw a bar model to show each calculation below.

a) 5 × 8 = 40

b) 80 ÷ 10 = 8

c) 8 × 8 = 64

**3**

Fill in the bar models and the calculations.

a)

40 ÷ ☐ = ☐

b)

| 8 | 8 | 8 | 8 |
|---|---|---|---|

☐ ÷ 4 = ☐

c)
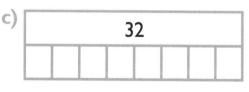

32 ÷ ☐ = ☐

**What a great find! Oscar stumbles upon a small pool of lava. Using his bucket, he scoops up some of the molten rock. Lava is a key ingredient for obsidian, which is needed for the Nether portal.**

**4**

Here are some sets of items. Write down the 8 times table facts you can use to find the total number of items.

a)

$\boxed{\phantom{0}} \times \boxed{\phantom{0}} = \boxed{\phantom{0}}$

$\boxed{\phantom{0}} \times \boxed{\phantom{0}} = \boxed{\phantom{0}}$

b)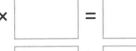

$\boxed{\phantom{0}} \times \boxed{\phantom{0}} = \boxed{\phantom{0}}$

$\boxed{\phantom{0}} \times \boxed{\phantom{0}} = \boxed{\phantom{0}}$

c)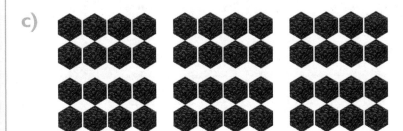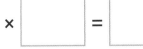

$\boxed{\phantom{0}} \times \boxed{\phantom{0}} = \boxed{\phantom{0}}$

$\boxed{\phantom{0}} \times \boxed{\phantom{0}} = \boxed{\phantom{0}}$

**5**

Oscar needs to split the following items into equal groups. Write and answer the calculations to divide each set of items into equal groups.

a) Divide 48 raw rabbit into 8 equal groups:   $\boxed{\phantom{0}} \div \boxed{\phantom{0}} = \boxed{\phantom{0}}$

b) Divide 56 rabbit hide into 7 equal groups:   $\boxed{\phantom{0}} \div \boxed{\phantom{0}} = \boxed{\phantom{0}}$

c) Divide 72 spruce saplings into 8 equal groups:   $\boxed{\phantom{0}} \div \boxed{\phantom{0}} = \boxed{\phantom{0}}$

d) Divide 32 spruce planks into 4 equal groups:   $\boxed{\phantom{0}} \div \boxed{\phantom{0}} = \boxed{\phantom{0}}$

# MENTAL MULTIPLICATION AND DIVISION

Oscar hasn't brought a bed with him to sleep through the night because he wants to fight some mobs and collect items from them – especially gunpowder from creepers and arrows from skeletons. He sits Moon next to the campfire to keep it safe. Oscar then grabs his sword, ready for battle.

 I

Draw a line from one multiplication in column A to an equivalent multiplication in column B. Do the same from column B to column C. In column C, write the answer to each set of equivalent multiplications you have found.

| A | B | C |
|---|---|---|
| 16 × 5 | 7 × 2 × 4 | 12 × 10 = ........... |
| 3 × 40 | 16 × 2 × 2 | 32 × 2 = ........... |
| 14 × 4 | 8 × 2 × 5 | 7 × 8 = ........... |
| 16 × 4 | 3 × 4 × 10 | 8 × 10 = ........... |

2

Fill in the boxes to show how you can use times tables facts, along with doubling or halving, to solve these questions. For example:

16 × 5 = 8 × 2 × 5 = 8 × 10 = 80

a) 11 × 6 = ☐ × 3 × 2 = ☐ × 2 = ☐

b) 20 × 8 = ☐ × 4 × 2 = ☐ × 2 = ☐

c) 12 × 6 = ☐ × 3 × 2 = ☐ × 2 = ☐

d) 7 × 30 = ☐ × 3 × 10 = ☐ × 10 = ☐

**3**

These calculations show swings of Oscar's sword. Change the order of the numbers in these calculations to make them easier to solve. Part of the first two have been done for you.

a) $5 \times 3 \times 12 = \boxed{\phantom{0}} \times 12 \times 3 = \boxed{\phantom{0}} \times 3 = \boxed{\phantom{0}}$

b) $9 \times 2 \times 3 = \boxed{\phantom{0}} \times \boxed{\phantom{0}} \times 2 = \boxed{\phantom{0}} \times 2 = \boxed{\phantom{0}}$

c) $2 \times 32 \times 5 = \boxed{\phantom{0}} \times \boxed{\phantom{0}} \times \boxed{\phantom{0}} = \boxed{\phantom{0}} \times \boxed{\phantom{0}} = \boxed{\phantom{0}}$

**4**

These calculations show the damage Oscar is doing to the skeletons. Use each given calculation to solve the related ones in the same row.

a) $8 \times 3 = 24$   $8 \times 30 = \boxed{\phantom{0}}$   $80 \times 3 = \boxed{\phantom{0}}$

b) $88 \div 8 = 11$   $880 \div 11 = \boxed{\phantom{0}}$   $880 \div 110 = \boxed{\phantom{0}}$

c) $12 \times 5 = 60$   $120 \times 5 = \boxed{\phantom{0}}$   $12 \times 50 = \boxed{\phantom{0}}$

**5**

 Write a fact family for the given multiplication. Completing each fact inflicts damage on a creeper.

Example:   Given that $4 \times 17 = 68$, then $40 \times 17 = 680$

Fact family:  $40 \times 17 = 680$       $17 \times 40 = 680$

$680 \div 17 = 40$       $680 \div 40 = 17$

Given that $3 \times 18 = 54$, then $3 \times 180 = \boxed{\phantom{0}}$

$\boxed{\phantom{0}} \times \boxed{\phantom{0}} = \boxed{\phantom{0}}$       $\boxed{\phantom{0}} \times \boxed{\phantom{0}} = \boxed{\phantom{0}}$

$\boxed{\phantom{0}} \div \boxed{\phantom{0}} = \boxed{\phantom{0}}$       $\boxed{\phantom{0}} \div \boxed{\phantom{0}} = \boxed{\phantom{0}}$

# MULTIPLYING TWO-DIGIT NUMBERS

Oscar takes a quick bite from a loaf of bread to keep up his health. Just as he does so, he's hit from behind. He turns to see an Enderman. It's coming right for him!

**1**

Partition the numbers, then multiply. An example has been done for you.

Example:

$$13 \times 2$$
$$10 \times 2 \quad + \quad 3 \times 2$$
$$= \qquad\qquad =$$
$$20 \quad + \quad 6$$
$$26$$

a)

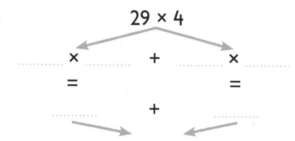

$$29 \times 4$$

b)

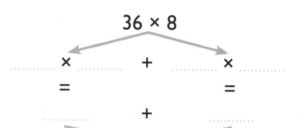

$$36 \times 8$$

c)

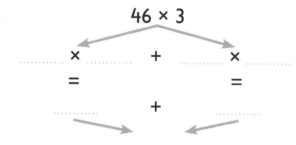

$$46 \times 3$$

d)

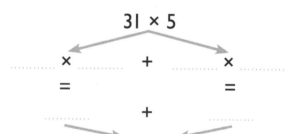

$$31 \times 5$$

**2**

Use a grid to multiply these numbers.

Example: 64 × 4 = 256

| × | 60 | 4 |
|---|-----|----|
| 4 | 240 | 16 |

a)  28 × 3 = ..........

| × | | |
|---|---|---|
| | | |

b)  24 × 8 = ..........

| × | | |
|---|---|---|
| | | |

c)  26 × 4 = ..........

| × | | |
|---|---|---|
| | | |

**Oscar eventually overcomes the Enderman but is worried that there are too many mobs for him to fight on his own. He runs back to the campfire and quickly builds a small wooden shelter to protect him and his wolf pup. He needs more to eat to regain health.**

**3**

Oscar calculates how many planks he needs for the shelter. Use the column method to multiply these numbers.

Example: 28 × 4 = 112

```
      2 8        or            2 8
  ×     4                  ×     4
  ─────────                ─────────
    1 1 2                      3 2
       3                  +    8 0
                          ─────────
                            1 1 2
```

a)
```
      4 8
  ×     4
  ─────────
```

b)
```
      2 3
  ×     3
  ─────────
```

c)
```
      3 7
  ×     8
  ─────────
```

d)
```
      3 1
  ×     4
  ─────────
```

**4**

Use the method you prefer to work out the total number in the groups described below.

a)  19 groups of 8

b)  58 groups of 3

c)  27 groups of 4

**COLOUR IN HOW MANY EMERALDS YOU EARNED**

# DIVIDING TWO-DIGIT NUMBERS

Oscar decides to stay in his shelter until morning. He doesn't have a bed to pass the time, so he removes a block from the wall and fights any passing mobs. The wolf pup is growing quickly and will soon be able to fight alongside him.

 I

Show how you can use place value counters and partitioning for each division. Then find the answer. For example: *88 ÷ 4*

| Tens | Ones |
|------|------|
| 10  10 | ● ● |
| 10  10 | ● ● |
| 10  10 | ● ● |
| 10  10 | ● ● |

*Be sure to share out the tens first.*

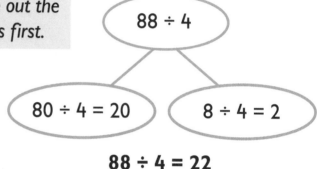

$$88 \div 4$$

$$80 \div 4 = 20 \qquad 8 \div 4 = 2$$

**88 ÷ 4 = 22**

a)  63 ÷ 3

| Tens | Ones |
|------|------|
|      |      |
|      |      |
|      |      |

b)  84 ÷ 4

| Tens | Ones |
|------|------|
|      |      |
|      |      |
|      |      |

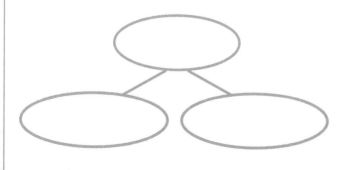

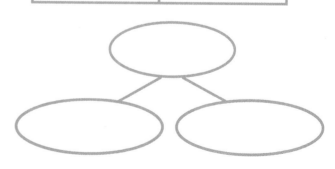

 **2**

If the number in the tens place is not a multiple of the number you are dividing by, you need to partition the numbers differently. For example: 42 ÷ 3

| Tens | Ones |
|------|------|
| 10 | ① ① ① ① |
| 10 | ① ① ① ① |
| 10 | ① ① ① ① |

*Share out the tens first. Then exchange the remaining tens for ones.*

42 ÷ 3

30 ÷ 3 = 10    12 ÷ 3 = 4

**42 ÷ 3 = 14**

Show how you can use place value counters and partitioning to answer each division.

a) 51 ÷ 3

| Tens | Ones |
|------|------|
|  |  |
|  |  |
|  |  |

b) 68 ÷ 4

| Tens | Ones |
|------|------|
|  |  |
|  |  |
|  |  |
|  |  |

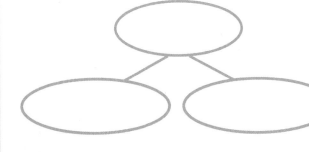

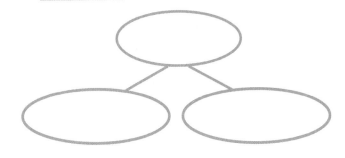

 **3**

Use the method you prefer to find each answer.

a) 85 ÷ 5     b) 76 ÷ 4     c) 60 ÷ 4     d) 95 ÷ 5

# WORD PROBLEMS

The sun has fully risen and Oscar breaks down his shelter. Overnight his pup Moon grew into an adult wolf. As Oscar arrives home, Maya is enjoying a game with their friends, Jacob and Cali. He joins in.

**1**

Oscar, Maya, Jacob and Cali are on the same team. They get 3 points for every arrow they fire into a target. Here are their points scores:

**Oscar 12      Maya 27      Jacob 15      Cali 18**

a) How many targets did each player hit?

Oscar: ☐     Maya: ☐     Jacob: ☐     Cali: ☐

b) How many targets did they hit altogether? ☐

c) How many more targets did Maya hit than Cali? ☐

d) They need a team total of 90 points to win the game. How many more targets do the team need to hit in order to win? ☐

**2**

Spiders have 8 legs. Llamas and horses have 4 legs. Oscar and Maya each have 2 legs. Oscar and Maya are with 5 spiders, 4 llamas and 3 horses.

How many legs are there in total? ☐

**3**

Oscar is splitting up his inventory items into equal groups. Find the number of items in each group.

a) 70 arrows split into 5 groups ☐

b) 69 feathers split into 3 groups ☐

c) 96 berries split into 8 groups ☐

# ADVENTURE ROUND-UP

## FURRY FRIEND

Oscar had a lot of fun exploring the new biome. After all that fighting, he's ready for some rest. He spends time separating his items and placing them into storage. The wolf barks a lot when Oscar walks past; they've obviously built up a close bond.

## PORTAL PLANS

Oscar is proud of himself for handling the mobs well and for working out the best plan while under pressure. Before going to bed, he sits with Maya to talk about building the Nether portal. Maya decides she will spend time tomorrow building it, while Oscar relaxes after a busy day.

## SWEET DREAMS

Oscar walks to his bedroom. His wolf follows. As Oscar lies down, the wolf curls up at the end of the bed. Before either of them knows it, they're fast asleep – one dreaming of chasing rabbits, the other dreaming about battling Endermen.

# FRACTIONS

## CLOSE TO NATURE

Back in the plains, Maya leaves the house. It's a beautiful day to be outside. Before she sets about her jobs for the day, she stands in the garden listening to the sounds around her. It's a peaceful moment; she hears a chicken clucking from behind the house and the wind rushing through the trees. Maya loves nature and she feels happy to be so close to it.

### PORTAL PREPARATION

Maya starts the day by feeding the farm animals. Her plan is to stay at home and begin work on the Nether portal. She picks out a spot near to the house for the portal. Maya plans to build a platform for the portal to sit on, as well as surrounding the area with a fence.

# TENTHS

Maya starts to build a raised platform for the Nether portal. She has chosen to use polished granite for the platform base, which will sit on columns. Maya begins by placing a 10 block by 10 block square.

**1**

Here is a plan which shows where 10 of the polished granite blocks can be placed:

| | | | | | | | | | |
|---|---|---|---|---|---|---|---|---|---|
| | | | | | | | | | |

a) Colour the blocks so that $\frac{3}{10}$ are red, $\frac{2}{10}$ are yellow, $\frac{1}{10}$ are blue and the rest are grey.

b) What fraction of the 10 squares are now coloured grey? ⬜

**2**

Fill in the missing fractions on this number line.

| 0 | $\frac{1}{10}$ | — | $\frac{3}{10}$ | — | $\frac{5}{10}$ | $\frac{6}{10}$ | — | — | $\frac{9}{10}$ | 1 |

**3**

Find one tenth of these quantities.

a) $\frac{1}{10}$ of 30 villagers

⬜ villagers

b) $\frac{1}{10}$ of 100 flowers

⬜ flowers

c) $\frac{1}{10}$ of 3 pumpkins

⬜ of a pumpkin

d) $\frac{1}{10}$ of 7 cakes

⬜ of a cake

# RECOGNISING FRACTIONS

Maya wants to add columns underneath the platform – one on each corner. She hunts through the supply chests to find a good building material. Remembering the terracotta from the badlands, she tries to decide between two colours.

**1**

a) Here is a row of 5 orange terracotta blocks:

What fraction of the row is circled? ▢ —

b) Here is a row of 3 yellow terracotta blocks:

What fraction of the row is circled? ▢ —

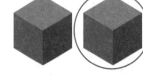

**2**

Here are 8 animals:

a) What fraction of the animals are cows? ▢ —

b) What fraction of the animals are pigs? ▢ —

Maya has built the granite platform; she has added orange terracotta columns below. It's time to start work on creating obsidian for the frame of the portal itself. To create obsidian, Maya must start by digging a large I × 7 block channel and pour a bucket of water into the middle. She then pours lava onto the water either side of the centre block.

**3**

a) Here is a channel, 7 blocks long, slowly filling with lava.

What fraction of the channel is filled with lava? $\dfrac{\phantom{0}}{\phantom{0}}$

b) Here is a channel, 9 blocks long, slowly filling with lava.

What fraction of the channel is filled with lava? $\dfrac{\phantom{0}}{\phantom{0}}$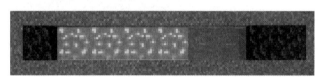

**4**

What fractions are the arrows pointing to on this number line?

$\dfrac{\phantom{0}}{\phantom{0}}$   $\dfrac{\phantom{0}}{\phantom{0}}$   $\dfrac{\phantom{0}}{\phantom{0}}$

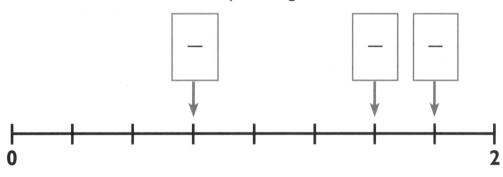

0                                                         2

**5**

Maya has 12 blocks of wood for the platform fence.

$\dfrac{1}{2}$ of the blocks are spruce, $\dfrac{1}{4}$ of the blocks are oak and the rest are birch.

How many of each block does she have?

Spruce: ⬜        Oak: ⬜        Birch: ⬜

# FRACTIONS OF AMOUNTS

Maya chooses spruce wood for the platform fence. She breaks down the logs into planks and one-third of those planks become sticks. Now Maya crafts them into a stack of spruce fences, ready to place. Around the columns, she decides to plant some flowers for decoration.

**1**

Here are 16 spruce fences:

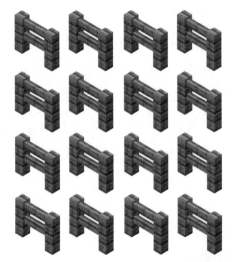

a) Draw a blue circle around $\frac{1}{4}$ of the fences.

b) Draw a red circle around $\frac{3}{4}$ of the fences.

c) Complete this sentence about the 16 fences:

$\frac{1}{4}$ of 16 is [     ] and $\frac{3}{4}$ of 16 is [     ] .

**2**

Find the fractions of these quantities.

a) $\frac{1}{5}$ of 15 orange tulips [     ] orange tulips

b) $\frac{1}{8}$ of 16 cornflowers [     ] cornflowers

c) $\frac{1}{3}$ of 12 lilacs [     ] lilacs

**3**

Maya had 9 carrots to keep away the hunger.

In the morning, she ate $\frac{1}{9}$ of the carrots.

For lunch, she ate $\frac{1}{4}$ of the remaining carrots.

In the afternoon, Maya ate $\frac{2}{3}$ of the remaining carrots.

How many carrots does she now have left? [     ]

As Maya works, she hears the sound of a sheep behind her. Turning to look over, she sees a creeper. She doesn't want it to explode and hurt her animals, so she defeats it quickly. Before going back to the fencing, Maya counts up all the nearby animals to make sure they are safe.

**4**

Find the fractions of these quantities.

a)  $\frac{3}{4}$ of 24 sheep  ⬜ sheep

b)  $\frac{2}{5}$ of 20 cows  ⬜ cows

c)  $\frac{3}{5}$ of 45 chickens  ⬜ chickens

d)  $\frac{2}{3}$ of 12 pigs  ⬜ pigs

**5**

Write **<**, **>** or **=** in the boxes to make these statements correct.

a)  $\frac{3}{4}$ of 12 sheep  ⬜  $\frac{1}{3}$ of 24 sheep

b)  $\frac{3}{8}$ of 16 cows  ⬜  $\frac{2}{5}$ of 20 cows

c)  $\frac{2}{3}$ of 18 chickens  ⬜  $\frac{4}{9}$ of 45 chickens

d)  $\frac{3}{4}$ of 24 pigs  ⬜  $\frac{1}{2}$ of 36 pigs

**COLOUR IN HOW MANY EMERALDS YOU EARNED**

49

# ADDITION AND SUBTRACTION OF FRACTIONS

After scooping up the remaining water into buckets, Maya is left with 14 blocks of obsidian. Now comes the hard part – mining the obsidian into separate blocks. Obsidian is a very tough material and can only be mined with a diamond pickaxe. Thankfully, Maya has one to hand.

**1**

Shade the shapes to match the calculations.

a) ☐☐☐ + ☐☐☐ = ☐☐☐        $\frac{1}{6} + \frac{3}{6} = \dfrac{\;\;}{\;\;}$

b) ☐☐ + ☐☐ = ☐☐        $\frac{1}{4} + \frac{2}{4} = \dfrac{\;\;}{\;\;}$

**2**

It takes a large number of pickaxe blows to mine the obsidian – it can't be done in one hit, it has to be done bit by bit.

Use the fraction bars to complete the calculations.

Example:
Calculate $\frac{5}{6} - \frac{2}{6}$

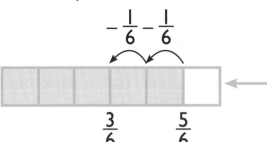

We can see from the fraction bar that
$\frac{5}{6} - \frac{2}{6} = \frac{3}{6}$

a) $\frac{2}{6} + \frac{3}{6} = \dfrac{\;\;}{\;\;}$

b) $\frac{7}{8} - \frac{3}{8} = \dfrac{\;\;}{\;\;}$

c) $\frac{5}{9} - \frac{4}{9} = \dfrac{\;\;}{\;\;}$

It's time to build the frame for the portal. Maya starts by placing 4 blocks in a row on the platform. On the end blocks, she builds up 3 and places another 4 blocks across the top.

**3**

Complete these calculations.

a) $\frac{2}{7} + \frac{3}{7} =$ ☐ —

b) $\frac{8}{14} - \frac{5}{14} =$ ☐ —

Oscar approaches Maya with 2 cakes to celebrate building the frame for the Nether portal.

**4**

Oscar and Maya divide the 2 cakes into 14 equal pieces.

a) If Oscar had 3 pieces and Maya had 2 pieces, what fraction of the 14 pieces would they have eaten in total? ☐ —

b) If Oscar had 4 pieces and Maya had 3 pieces, what fraction of the 14 pieces would be left? ☐ —

c) If Oscar had 7 of the 14 pieces and Maya had 3, what fraction more would Oscar have had than Maya? ☐ —

**5**

 Fill in the missing fractions.

a) $\frac{3}{8} +$ ☐ — $= \frac{7}{8}$

b) ☐ — $- \frac{3}{8} = \frac{4}{8}$

# EQUIVALENT FRACTIONS

Here is a diagram that shows some equivalent fractions:

| 1 | | | | | | | |
|---|---|---|---|---|---|---|---|
| $\frac{1}{2}$ | | | | $\frac{1}{2}$ | | | |
| $\frac{1}{4}$ | | $\frac{1}{4}$ | | $\frac{1}{4}$ | | $\frac{1}{4}$ | |
| $\frac{1}{8}$ | $\frac{1}{8}$ | $\frac{1}{8}$ | $\frac{1}{8}$ | $\frac{1}{8}$ | $\frac{1}{8}$ | $\frac{1}{8}$ | $\frac{1}{8}$ |
| $\frac{1}{5}$ | | $\frac{1}{5}$ | | $\frac{1}{5}$ | | $\frac{1}{5}$ | $\frac{1}{5}$ |
| $\frac{1}{10}$ $\frac{1}{10}$ | $\frac{1}{10}$ $\frac{1}{10}$ | $\frac{1}{10}$ $\frac{1}{10}$ | $\frac{1}{10}$ $\frac{1}{10}$ | $\frac{1}{10}$ $\frac{1}{10}$ | | | |

**1**

Write the equivalent fractions shown in each row.

a)
  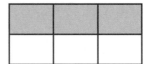  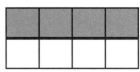

$\dfrac{\phantom{0}}{\phantom{0}} = \dfrac{\phantom{0}}{\phantom{0}} = \dfrac{\phantom{0}}{\phantom{0}} = \dfrac{\phantom{0}}{\phantom{0}}$

b)
    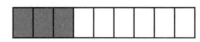  

$\dfrac{\phantom{0}}{\phantom{0}} = \dfrac{\phantom{0}}{\phantom{0}} = \dfrac{\phantom{0}}{\phantom{0}}$

**2**

In each image, shade in one half. Write the fraction shaded in each box.

a) 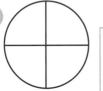 $\dfrac{\phantom{0}}{4}$

b)  $\dfrac{\phantom{0}}{8}$

c)  $\dfrac{\phantom{0}}{6}$

d) 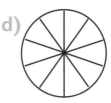 $\dfrac{\phantom{0}}{10}$

**Maya has decided to make a fun new building using different colours of terracotta. Oscar wonders what will go inside. Maya had a few ideas but settles on this building being an enchanting room. Maya has collected a lot of terracotta blocks in different shades and she will use them to make colourful patterns on the floors and walls.**

**3**

You can find equivalent fractions by multiplying the numerator and the denominator by the same number.

Example:

$$\overset{\times 2}{\overset{\frown}{\underset{\underset{\times 2}{\smile}}{\frac{3}{4}}}} = \frac{6}{8}$$

Complete these chains of equivalent fractions.

a)

$$\overset{\times 2 \quad \times 2}{\frac{1}{2} = \frac{2}{\Box} = \frac{4}{\Box}}$$
$$\times 2 \quad \times 2$$

$$\frac{1}{3} = \frac{2}{\Box} = \frac{4}{\Box}$$

$$\frac{2}{5} = \frac{\Box}{10} = \frac{\Box}{20}$$

b)

$$\overset{\div 2 \quad \div 2}{\frac{16}{20} = \frac{8}{\Box} = \frac{4}{\Box}}$$
$$\div 2 \quad \div 2$$

$$\frac{8}{12} = \frac{4}{\Box} = \frac{2}{\Box}$$

$$\frac{40}{100} = \frac{\Box}{50} = \frac{\Box}{25}$$

**4**

Complete these equivalent fractions.

a) $\frac{1}{5} = \frac{\Box}{15} = \frac{\Box}{30}$

b) $\frac{2}{3} = \frac{6}{\Box} = \frac{12}{\Box}$

c) $\frac{2}{4} = \frac{8}{\Box} = \frac{16}{\Box}$

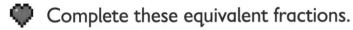

**COLOUR IN HOW MANY EMERALDS YOU EARNED**

# COMPARING AND ORDERING FRACTIONS

Maya places bookcases around the inside walls of the enchanting room. More bookcases mean more powerful enchantments can be used on tools or weapons.

**1**

Shade the shapes and then draw a circle around the larger fraction in each pair.

a)

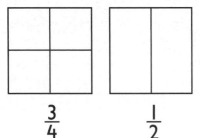

$\frac{3}{4}$ $\frac{1}{2}$

b)

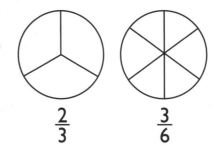

$\frac{2}{3}$ $\frac{3}{6}$

**2**

Shade these shapes to represent the fractions written beside them. Then write **>**, **<** or **=** in the box.

a) $\frac{1}{3}$  $\frac{4}{6}$ $\frac{1}{3}$ ☐ $\frac{4}{6}$

b) $\frac{1}{2}$ 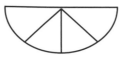 $\frac{3}{4}$ $\frac{1}{2}$ ☐ $\frac{3}{4}$

c) $\frac{5}{8}$ 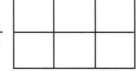 $\frac{1}{2}$ $\frac{5}{8}$ ☐ $\frac{1}{2}$

d) $\frac{3}{5}$  $\frac{6}{10}$ $\frac{3}{5}$ ☐ $\frac{6}{10}$

For the final part of the room, Maya needs an enchanting table. To craft this she needs: 1 book, 2 diamonds and 4 blocks of obsidian. In order to use the table, the heroes trade their experience levels along with a chunk of lapis lazuli. Maya makes sure everything is in place. She decides to test the table on a few tools and weapons.

**3**

To enchant this iron sword with Smite I, write these fractions in order from smallest to largest.

$\frac{1}{6}$ $\quad$ $\frac{1}{4}$ $\quad$ $\frac{1}{3}$ $\quad$ $\frac{1}{5}$ $\quad$ $\frac{2}{3}$ $\quad$ $\frac{5}{6}$

**4**

To enchant this iron chestplate with Fire Protection II, write these fractions on the number line: $\frac{1}{4}$ $\quad$ $\frac{1}{10}$ $\quad$ $\frac{3}{5}$ $\quad$ $\frac{1}{2}$

0 ├─────────────────────────────────────────┤ 1

**5**

 To enchant this diamond pickaxe with Fortune I, write >, < or = in each box to make the statements true. Use the diagram on page 52 to help.

a) $\frac{2}{8}$ ☐ $\frac{1}{10}$ $\qquad$ b) $\frac{3}{7}$ ☐ $\frac{6}{14}$

c) $\frac{3}{4}$ ☐ $\frac{4}{5}$ $\qquad$ d) $\frac{3}{5}$ ☐ $\frac{1}{2}$

 **COLOUR IN HOW MANY EMERALDS YOU EARNED**

# FRACTION PROBLEMS

Maya stands back to admire her work on the enchanting room and the Nether portal. The only thing missing is a roof on the enchanting room.

**1**

Maya is building a roof using 20 oak stairs for the angled shape. She has completed $\frac{3}{10}$ of the roof.

a)   How many oak stairs has Maya installed?

b)   What fraction of the roof does she have left to complete? ⬚ — ⬚

**2**

Work out these quantities.

a)   Oscar has $\frac{1}{5}$ of the number of wheat that Maya has. Maya has 35 wheat.

How many wheat does Oscar have? ⬚

b)   Oscar has $\frac{1}{3}$ of the sugar cane that Maya has. Oscar has 9 sugar cane.

How many sugar cane does Maya have? ⬚

**3**

Maya has planted 12 peony flowers outside the enchanting room.

a)   Maya thinks that $\frac{1}{4}$ of the flowerbed is more than $\frac{1}{3}$ of the flowerbed because 4 is bigger than 3. Is she correct? Explain your answer.

...............................................................................................................

...............................................................................................................

Maya removes $\frac{1}{6}$ of the 12 flowers and Oscar takes $\frac{3}{6}$ of them.

b)   What fraction of the flowerbed is left? ⬚ — ⬚

c)   How many flowers are left standing? ⬚

**COLOUR IN HOW MANY EMERALDS YOU EARNED**

# ADVENTURE ROUND-UP

## A DAY OF ACHIEVEMENT

Maya has done a great job today. She built a platform for the Nether portal, the frame for it and a whole new room for enchanting tools. She has already traded some of her experience points for great enchantments on some of her equipment. These will really help in future.

## DOORWAY TO ANOTHER DIMENSION

Both heroes look out towards the obsidian frame they have prepared for the Nether portal. All they need to do is light it, using a flint and steel. Once lit, a purple doorway will appear within the frame. By standing in the purple shimmer, they will be transported to the Nether – a very dangerous dimension, full of mobs and important materials.

## WHAT LIES AHEAD?

Before Maya and Oscar head to their bedrooms to rest, they decide that tomorrow they will enter the portal. They're both a little nervous, but they know that by using the skills they have learned so far, they'll be fine. As Maya drifts off to sleep, she wonders what tomorrow will bring.

# MEASUREMENT

## WHAT AWAITS?

Oscar and Maya have used a flint and steel to light the Nether portal. The gate activates with a purple shimmer. As they step forward into the glow, they tighten their grip on their swords and prepare for new experiences. The purple light fades and the heroes find themselves in the Nether wastes.

## BE PREPARED

The Nether is a dark and dangerous place. The wastes are the most common biome; the ground is made of a red rock called netherrack. There are no rivers – in fact, there is no water at all. All that flows through the Nether is lava. No hero should enter the Nether unprepared – everything here is designed to hurt and one false move could be fatal.

## HOSTILE ENVIRONMENT

Zombified piglins, armed with golden swords, will mind their own business unless provoked. The ghasts which hover through the air may look cute at first, but they will blast fireballs from their mouths. Then there are the Wither skeletons, the blazes and the magma cubes: all dangerous and difficult to fight.

## RIDE A STRIDER

Mobs called striders are happy in the lava. They will even carry adventurers when fitted with a saddle and controlled using a fishing rod with a warped fungus.

# READING SCALES

Length is measured in millimetres (mm), centimetres (cm) and metres (m).

Mass is measured in grams (g) and kilograms (kg).

Capacity is how much a container can hold. Volume is how much is in the container. They are both measured in millilitres (ml) and litres (l).

Netherrack (which is like solid rock), Nether quartz (an ore) and lava can be seen as Oscar and Maya step into the Nether wastes.

**1** Use a ruler to measure the length of this line of netherrack blocks in centimetres.

[ ] cm

**2** Read the scales to find the mass of this Nether quartz.

[ ] g

**3** Some of the lava is shown in this container:

a) What is the capacity of the container?

[ ] litres

b) What is the volume of lava in the container?

[ ] ml

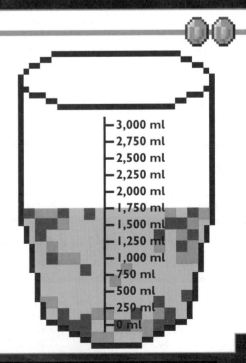

# COMPARING MEASURES

| | | |
|---|---|---|
| **Length:** 10 mm = 1 cm | 100 cm = 1 m | 1,000 m = 1 km |
| **Mass / Weight:** 1,000 g = 1 kg | | |
| **Capacity:** 1,000 ml = 1 l | | |

Oscar and Maya decide to split up, in order to cover more of the Nether between them. They will meet back at the portal later.

**1**

Draw lines to join up the equivalent measurements in each column.

a)

| | |
|---|---|
| 1 m 50 cm | 1,500 m |
| 300 cm | 150 cm |
| 1 km 500 m | 3 cm |
| 30 mm | 3 m |

b)

| | |
|---|---|
| 3,000 ml | 0.5 l |
| 500 ml | 3 l |
| 5,000 ml | 30 l |
| 30,000 ml | 5 l |

c)

| | |
|---|---|
| 3 kg | 2,050 g |
| 2 kg 500 g | 3,000 g |
| 3 kg 500 g | 2,500 g |
| 2 kg 50 g | 3,500 g |

**2**

Circle the item in each pair with the larger distance, mass or capacity.

a)
2,500 m   3 km

b)
2 kg   1,500 g

c)
3,250 ml   5 l

Oscar is mining, chopping and digging. He has already found some really interesting materials and items, and he can see plenty more to investigate.

**3**

35 cm and 7 mm        3 cm and 7 mm           317 cm           3 m and 7 cm

Order the lengths from shortest to longest.

| | | | |
|---|---|---|---|
| | < | < | < |

**4**

Write down the mass of each item. Then order the masses from lightest to heaviest.

Mass: ............    Mass: ............    Mass: ............    Mass: ............

| | | | |
|---|---|---|---|
| | < | < | < |

# ADDING AND SUBTRACTING MEASURES

You can use models or portioning to add and subtract measurements.

I kg and 200 g + 2 kg and 400 g = 3 kg and 600 g

I kg and 200 g + 2 kg and 400 g

= I kg + 2 kg + 200 g + 400g

= 3 kg + 600 g

3 km and 250 m – I km and 120 m = 2 km 130 m

| 3 km | |
|---|---|
| I km | ? km |

3 km – I km = 2 km

| 250 m | |
|---|---|
| 120 m | ? m |

250 m – 120 m = 130 m

Oscar can see something in the distance that interests him, but he must navigate a lot of lava to reach it. He can build a path using some cobblestone he brought. Help him to find the best route.

**I**

This plan shows the routes that Oscar can take to get around the lava.

Find the shortest route from point A to point B.

What is the distance?

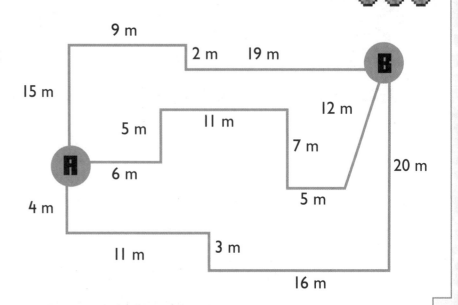

m

Oscar safely gets around the lava. What he could see was glowstone hanging from the ceiling of the wastes. It's bright and beautiful. He builds a column upwards to harvest it. When harvested, the glowstone crumbles to dust: four of these combined will create a glowstone block.

**2**

Work out these calculations.

a)  1 kg and 220 g + 2 kg and 410 g = .............................................

b)  2 l and 500 ml + 5 l and 205 ml = .............................................

c)  4 km and 710 m + 2 km and 105 m = .............................................

d)  5 km and 360 m – 4 km and 140 m = .............................................

e)  8 kg and 900 g – 3 kg and 350 g = .............................................

f)  3 cm and 7 mm – 2 cm and 5 mm = .............................................

**3**

a)  Oscar has walked a total of 6 km 600 m today. In the morning he walked 4 km 250 m.

How far has he walked since the morning? .............................................

b)  Oscar has been working so hard that he has lost some weight. He once weighed 78 kg 500 g but now he weighs 73 kg 750 g.

How much weight has he lost? .............................................

# MONEY

Mobs called piglins live in the Nether. They love anything made of gold. Oscar even has to be wearing something gold, or they'll attack. They're happy to barter items for gold ingots with any adventurer. See if your money skills are as good as gold.

**1**

How much money is shown in each row?

a)           Total: ................

b)           Total: ................

c)           Total: ................

d)           Total: ................

**2**

Add these amounts of money.

a)  £2 and 35p + £5 and 17p =  ...............

b)  £4 and 74p + £10 and 19p =  ...............

c)  £9 and 29p + £3 and 15p =  ...............

d)  £12 and 56p + £7 and 31p =  ...............

Oscar mines patches of Nether gold wherever he sees it. This will be helpful when he finally meets the piglins; he's hoping to trade the gold for lots of Ender pearls, which will be important for future missions. As Oscar is busy digging, suddenly an explosion knocks him sideways!

**3**

Subtract these amounts of money.

a) £25 and 96p – £6 and 65p = ...........................................

b) £3 and 45p – £2 and 6p = ...........................................

c) £8 and 20p – £6 and 8p = ...........................................

d) £11 and 61p – £5 and 42p = ...........................................

**4**

Look at the cost of these items:

a) How much do the items cost in total?

......................................................

b) A customer buys all the items and pays with a £10 note.

How much change do they receive?

......................................................

£1 and 32p

£3 and 64p

£4 and 26p

# TIME

As Oscar gets back to his feet, he sees a ball of fire speeding towards him. He gets out of the way just in time and the ground explodes into chunks. Oscar sees a ghast hovering close by, as another fireball whizzes through the air. Oscar swings his sword in shock and to his surprise he bats the fireball back at the ghast!

**1**

What time is shown on these analogue clocks? Write the time in numbers and in words for each of them.

a)

:

....................  ....................

b)

:

....................  ....................

....................................................................

c)

:

....................  ....................

d)

:

....................  ....................

....................................................................

Oscar has perfect timing. He keeps hitting the fireballs back towards the ghast using his sword. BOOM! The ghast has been defeated and Oscar sees a small white teardrop fall from it. It's a ghast tear – something else to take home and experiment with.

**2**

Draw the hands on the analogue clocks to show the times.

a)   2:29     b)   4:53     c)   5:08     d)   10:32

**3**

Write the time shown on these clocks in words.

a)     b)

......................................    ......................................

**4**

Complete the missing information for the two times given.

a)     b)

**Analogue clock:**

**Time in words:** ............ minutes past ............ in the evening     quarter to five in the morning

**24-hour digital clock:** ......... : .........     ......... : .........

COLOUR IN HOW MANY EMERALDS YOU EARNED

67

# UNITS OF TIME

::::::::::::::::::::::::::::::::::::::::::::::::::::::::::::::::::::::::::::::::::::::::::::::::::::::::::::

I minute = 60 seconds    I hour = 60 minutes        I day = 24 hours
I week = 7 days           I year = 365 days (366 in a leap year)
The date is usually written in a format of day/month/year.

Time doesn't pass by in the same way for Oscar as it does in our world. A day for Oscar is only 20 minutes for us. He'd love to take a nap, but he can't sleep in a bed in the Nether because they explode! While he takes a few moments to eat and restore his health, take your time with these questions.

a)  Write these dates in words.

The third day of the fourth month. .............................................................

The last day of the year. .............................................................

The first day of the sixth month. .............................................................

The last day of the eighth month. .............................................................

b)  Order the dates above from the earliest to the latest in the year.

.............................................................................................................

.............................................................................................................

**2**

Complete these time conversions.

a)  20 hours = ☐ minutes        b)  2 days = ☐ hours

c)  120 seconds = ☐ minutes     d)  3 minutes = ☐ seconds

e)  21 days = ☐ weeks           f)  600 minutes = ☐ hours

**3**

Use the calendar to answer these questions.

| | March | | | | | | |
|---|---|---|---|---|---|---|
| **Mon** | **Tue** | **Wed** | **Thu** | **Fri** | **Sat** | **Sun** |
| 1 | 2 | 3 | 4 | 5 | 6 | 7 |
| 8 | 9 | 10 | 11 | 12 | 13 | 14 |
| 15 | 16 | 17 | 18 | 19 | 20 | 21 |
| 22 | 23 | 24 | 25 | 26 | 27 | 28 |
| 29 | 30 | 31 | | | | |

a) Oscar visits a nearby village for supplies on the fourth Thursday of March.

On what date does he visit the village for supplies?

..............................................

b) He organises the storage chests every Wednesday.

How many times in the month does he organise the storage chests? ..............................................

c) Oscar will explore another biome in the Nether one week from now.

If today is the 8th, what day and date will he explore the other biome?

..............................................

**4**

♥ Fill in the boxes with **<**, **>** or **=** to make each statement true.

a) 240 seconds ☐ 3 minutes

b) 6 hours ☐ 600 minutes

c) 30 days ☐ number of days in February

d) 36 hours ☐ 2 days

# DURATION OF EVENTS

In the Nether, there's not much time to relax or take it easy because you never know when a mob will attack.

**1**

Find the duration of these events in hours and minutes.

a) **Feed the farm animals**    Starts at 6:30 pm    Finishes at 7:30 pm

b) **Eat dinner**    Starts at 4:15 pm    Finishes at 5:30 pm

c) **Harvest crops**    Starts at 7:15 am    Finishes at 8:45 am

**2**

Oscar has this routine when he's at home.

Eat breakfast: (morning)    Check the smelters: (morning)    Cook food: (afternoon)    Patrol for mobs: (evening)

a) How long is the time between eating breakfast and checking the smelters?

b) How long is the time between checking the smelters and cooking food?

c) How long is the time between eating breakfast and patrolling for mobs?

**Oscar's inventory is getting full of all the great materials he has found. He makes his way back to the portal to see if Maya is waiting for him. When he reaches the portal, he finds a sign with a note from Maya which reads: "Found a fortress! Going to explore. Meet at the house."**

**3**

Which event ends at the later time?

A game starts at quarter past 3 in the afternoon and lasts 50 minutes.

Vegetable harvest starts at 2:45 pm and lasts for 1 hour and 10 minutes.

..............................................................................................

**4**

Work out the times for these events.

a) Lunch starts at 12:30 in the afternoon and takes 50 minutes.

At what time does it finish? ...............................................

b) A cave exploration starts at 10:35 am and takes 1 hour and 20 minutes.

At what time does it finish? ...............................................

c) Sheep shearing takes 45 minutes and finishes at 3:30 pm.

At what time did it start? ...............................................

d) A smelting session takes 23 minutes and finishes at 5:52 pm.

At what time did it start? ...............................................

**5**

Oscar began his walk back to the Nether portal at 1:51 in the afternoon.

He took a half-hour break at 2:55 pm. He then continued walking for another 25 minutes to get to the portal.

At what time did he arrive at the portal? ...............................................

**COLOUR IN HOW MANY EMERALDS YOU EARNED**

71

# PERIMETER OF SHAPES

The perimeter is the total length around the edge of a shape.

Oscar steps into the portal. The purple shimmer surrounds him and within a few seconds he finds himself standing in front of the perimeter fence of his garden.

**1**

Measure the perimeter of the rectangles.

a)

☐ cm

b)

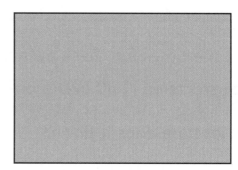

☐ cm

**2**

Here are some regular polygons – the sides of each shape are the same length. Measure one side. Then work out the perimeter of the shape.

a)
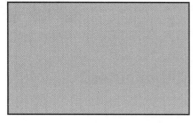

☐ cm

b)

☐ cm

c)

☐ cm

d)

☐ cm

**COLOUR IN HOW MANY EMERALDS YOU EARNED**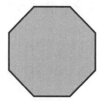

# ADVENTURE ROUND-UP

## INTERESTING INVENTORY

After his trip to the Nether, Oscar's inventory is bursting with interesting things. Some of the materials he has found could be useful for crafting potions.

## WHERE'S MAYA?

Before eating dinner, Oscar re-forms the glowstone blocks from the dust he harvested and places them around the house. He thinks it looks much better than torches. As Oscar goes about his evening, he can't help but worry about Maya. Surely she should be back by now?

# GEOMETRY AND STATISTICS

## NETHER FORTRESS FOUND

Maya left Oscar to explore other parts of the Nether wastes. She has seen what looks to be a large building in the distance. It's a Nether fortress. As Maya finds an opening to squeeze through, all she can hear is squelching, groaning and an odd clicking sound from within.

## MYSTERIOUS PAST

Nobody knows who the Nether fortress was originally built for. Maya wonders if it was where the Wither (a three-headed boss mob) once lived, because the fortress hallways are full of Wither skeletons. The fortress feels like a maze on the inside. Corridors lead in all directions to rooms or dead-ends. Among the staircases and empty rooms, chests might be found with some leftover loot inside.

## DANGER ALL AROUND

There's no light inside a fortress, so hostile mobs gather here. Even the best adventurers can struggle against so many. Wither skeletons will fire arrows and a blaze will shoot fireballs. Magma cubes bounce around and break apart with each piece attacking. And as soon as the hero thinks they're winning, a Wither skeleton may hit them from behind and curse them.

# ANGLES AND TURNS

Maya enters a dark corridor. She has some torches and she pulls out her compass to check her position. The needle on her compass whirls around and around. It doesn't work in the Nether.

## 1

Maya is facing north. What direction is she facing after each of these turns?

a)   Quarter turn clockwise   ..............................................

b)   Half turn clockwise   ..............................................

c)   Three-quarter turn clockwise   ..............................................

d)   Quarter turn anti-clockwise   ..............................................

## 2

How many right-angle turns would Maya need to make for these movements?

a)   She starts facing east and turns to face south.

☐ right-angle turn(s) clockwise or ☐ right-angle turn(s) anti-clockwise.

b)   She starts facing west and turns to face south.

☐ right-angle turn(s) clockwise or ☐ right-angle turn(s) anti-clockwise.

## 3

Write a program for a robot to scout a corridor for Maya. A plan of the corridor is shown. The robot is already facing down the corridor.

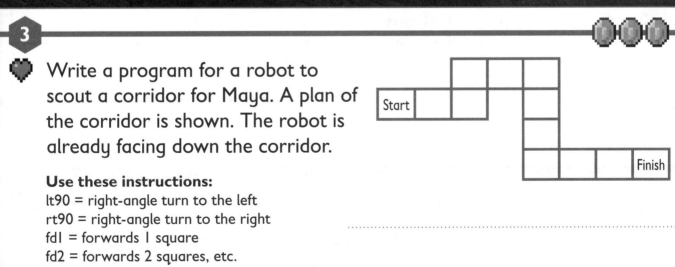

**Use these instructions:**
lt90 = right-angle turn to the left
rt90 = right-angle turn to the right
fd1 = forwards 1 square
fd2 = forwards 2 squares, etc.

..............................................................

..............................................................

# TYPES OF ANGLES

The inside of the fortress is very confusing. Maya is trying to leave a trail of torches and remember which turns she has made.

**1**

Sort these angles labelled A–F into acute, obtuse and right angles.

A

B

C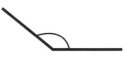

D

E

F

| Acute | Right | Obtuse |
|-------|-------|--------|
|       |       |        |
|       |       |        |

**2**

Order the angles A–F in question 1 by size from smallest to largest.

 <  <  <  <  <

**Maya spots a chest. Inside there are a few things to help her – 2 diamonds, 1 gold horse armour, 1 saddle and a flint and steel – but she thinks that there may be more valuables further inside the fortress.**

**3**

Look at this diagram. Label the acute angles 'A', the obtuse angles 'O' and the right angles 'R'.

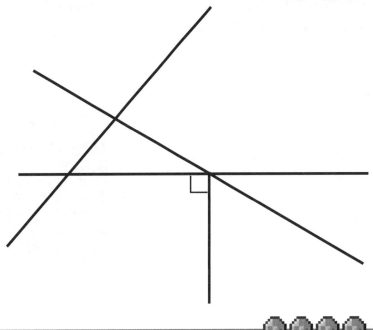

**4**

Draw lines to join each shape to its correct description.

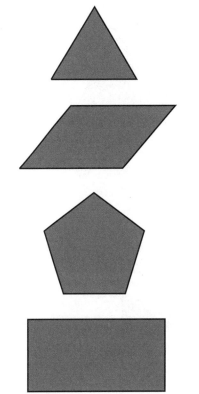

I have four right angles.

I have two acute and two obtuse angles.

All my angles are obtuse.

All my angles are acute.

# LINES

Maya finds a strange plant growing next to a staircase. It's Nether wart – an important ingredient for potion making! It is growing in soul sand so she will need to take some of this too in order to grow more Nether wart at home.

**1**

Use a ruler to draw horizontal lines and vertical lines over the rows of Nether wart in this picture.

**2**

Draw the lines of symmetry on these shapes. Write whether you have drawn horizontal or vertical lines of symmetry, or both.

a)
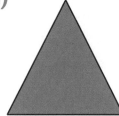

...........................

...........................

b)

...........................

...........................

c)

...........................

...........................

d)

...........................

...........................

e)

...........................

...........................

f)

...........................

...........................

As Maya walks on, she hears a strange sound coming from the end of a corridor. She can see a light from where the sound is coming. Being brave, she decides to investigate.

**3**

Find two pairs of parallel lines and two pairs of perpendicular lines on this flag. You could mark the parallel lines in one colour and the perpendicular lines in another colour.

**4**

Complete the sentences about the octagon shown by writing the correct line (AB, BC, CD, etc.) in each answer space.

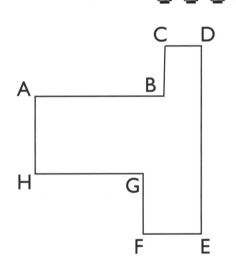

a) Line ............................ is one of the lines that is parallel to line AB.

b) Line ............................ is one of the lines that is perpendicular to line AB.

c) Line ............................ is one of the lines that is parallel to line CD.

d) Line ............................ is one of the lines that is perpendicular to line CD.

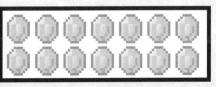

# 2-D SHAPES

Maya wishes she hadn't walked down the corridor. She comes face to face with several blazes that start launching fireballs at her. She notices there's a spawner in the middle of them. Unless Maya breaks that, they'll keep spawning.

**1**

Use four different colours to show the different polygons that make up this picture of Maya's sword. Complete the key to show which colour you have used for each shape.

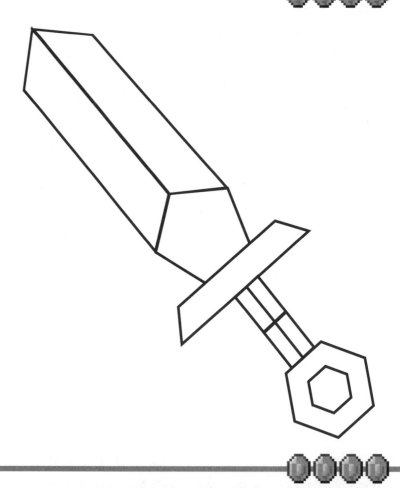

**Key:**

Rectangles

Quadrilaterals
(excluding
rectangles)

Hexagons

Pentagons

**2**

How many sides in total are on:

a)   four octagons?

b)   five hexagons?

c)   twelve squares?

d)   nine pentagons?

Maya suffers a lot of hits and has to keep backing off to heal. Eventually, she gets through and breaks the blaze spawner. After fighting so many blazes, Maya has lots of blaze rods – another important ingredient for potion making.

**3**

Complete the sentences to describe this shape.

a) The shape has [ ] side(s).

It has [ ] pair(s) of parallel sides.

b) The shape has [ ] acute angle(s).

It has [ ] obtuse angle(s).

It has [ ] right angle(s).

c) The shape has [ ] horizontal line(s) of symmetry.

It has [ ] vertical line(s) of symmetry.

**4**

Draw lines to join each quadrilateral to its description.

I have two pairs of parallel sides and two lines of symmetry.

I have four equal sides and two lines of symmetry.

I have two pairs of parallel sides and no lines of symmetry.

I have one pair of parallel sides.

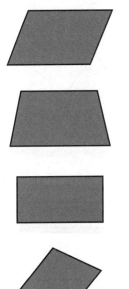

COLOUR IN HOW MANY EMERALDS YOU EARNED

# 3-D SHAPES

Maya is worried about meeting any more mobs. She begins to make her way out of the Nether fortress by following the torches she placed. Maya is happy with the items she discovered and can't wait to use them.

**1**

a)  Add the labels **face**, **edge** and **vertex** to this cube.

b)  A cube has ☐ faces,

☐ edges and ☐ vertices.

**2**

Sort the shapes A–F by writing each letter in the correct part of the table.

A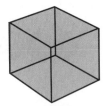

B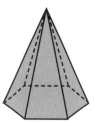

C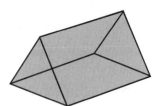

D

E

F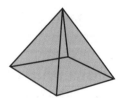

| | Even number of vertices | Odd number of vertices | No vertices |
|---|---|---|---|
| **Prism** | | | |
| **Not a prism** | | | |

There's something blocking the exit. It looks like a skeleton. Maya has no choice; she has to fight again. But it's no ordinary skeleton – it's holding a sword, not a bow. It's a **Wither skeleton!** Maya runs in, sword swinging!

**3**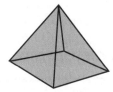

Complete the table to describe shapes A–D.

A    B 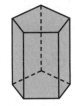   C 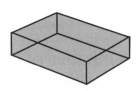   D

|  | Shape A | Shape B | Shape C | Shape D |
|---|---|---|---|---|
| Name of 3-D shape |  |  |  |  |
| Prism or pyramid? |  |  |  |  |
| Number of vertices |  |  |  |  |
| Number of faces |  |  |  |  |
| Number of edges |  |  |  |  |

**4**

Work out what shapes are being described.

a) It has 5 faces, 6 vertices and 9 edges. It is made up of triangles and rectangles.

......................................................................

b) It has 2 faces, 1 edge and 1 vertex. One of its faces is a circle.

......................................................................

**COLOUR IN HOW MANY EMERALDS YOU EARNED**

# PICTOGRAMS

Maya defeats the Wither skeleton, but she gets hit by its sword towards the end of the fight. Her health bar hearts have turned from red to black. This is the Wither effect and it eats away at her health. Maya needs to find safety and eat to restore her health.

**1**

This pictogram shows the number of mobs that Maya saw each day.

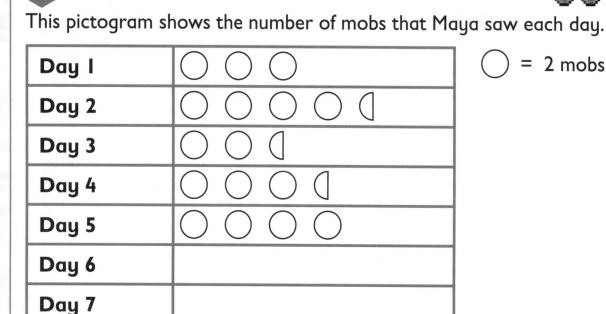

○ = 2 mobs

a)  On which day did she see the greatest number of mobs?

b)  How many more mobs did she see on that day than on day 3?

c)  On day 6, she saw half as many mobs as she saw on day 1. Fill in the pictogram.

d)  On day 7, Maya saw one less mob than she saw on day 5. Fill in the pictogram.

e)  How many mobs in total did she see on days 3 and 4?

**2**

Complete the table to show the data in question 1.

| Day | 1 | 2 | 3 | 4 | 5 | 6 | 7 |
|---|---|---|---|---|---|---|---|
| Number of mobs seen | | | | | | | |

The **Wither** effect reduces Maya to half a heart, but resting for a while and eating helps to restore some health. Maya runs to the portal as fast as she can. From tomorrow she will start growing the Nether wart.

**3**

This table shows the number of Nether wart in five plots.

| Plot | A | B | C | D | E |
|---|---|---|---|---|---|
| Number of Nether wart | 12 | 15 | 18 | 6 | 9 |

Complete this pictogram to show the data given in the table.

 = 2 Nether wart

| | |
|---|---|
| **Plot A** | |
| **Plot B** | |
| **Plot C** | |
| **Plot D** | |
| **Plot E** | |

**4**

Complete the sentences about the data in question 3.

a) The smallest number of Nether wart is in plot ☐ .

b) In plot B, there are ☐ more Nether wart than in plot E.

c) In plot C, there are ☐ times more Nether wart than in plot D.

d) In total, there are ☐ Nether wart.

# BAR CHARTS

Oscar meets Maya as she steps out of the Nether portal and returns to the Overworld. He had been getting worried about her. Together they walk back home.

**1**

This bar chart shows the number of items Maya sees around the home. The bar for melon has not yet been added to it.

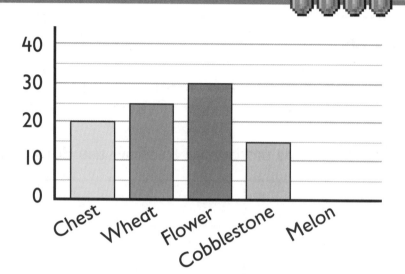

a)   Which item does Maya see the most? ......................................................

b)   How many more flowers does she see than chests?

c)   Maya sees 20 fewer melons than flowers.
Add a bar to the chart to show the number of melons she sees.

d)   How many items in total does she see?

**2**

Complete this table to show the data in question 1.

| Item | Chest | Wheat | Flower | Cobblestone | Melon |
|---|---|---|---|---|---|
| **Number of items** | | | | | |

**3**

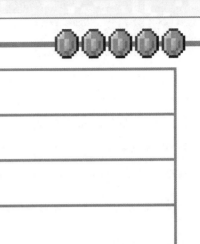

Complete this pictogram to show the data in question 1.

◯ = 10 items

| Chest | |
|---|---|
| Wheat | |
| Flower | |
| Cobblestone | |
| Melon | |

**4**

This pictogram shows the quantities of some of the food items in the house. There are 80 bread in total.

| Bread | ☐ ☐ ☐ ☐ |
|---|---|
| Carrots | ☐ ☐ ☐ ☐ |
| Apples | ☐ ☐ ☐ |
| Beetroot | ☐ ☐ ☐ ☐ ☐ |

☐ = ................

a) Complete the key for the pictogram.

b) Draw a bar chart to show the data.

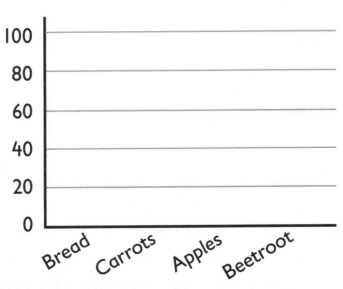

# TABLES

Maya and Oscar are admiring all the items they collected. Before they ever go back to the Nether, they want to enchant more armour and weapons, and craft some potions using a brewing stand.

**1**

This table shows information about four potions that they have crafted.

| Potion | Colour | Bottles made | Value |
|---|---|---|---|
| Potion of Leaping | Green | 6 | 60 emeralds |
| Potion of Healing | Red | 2 | 40 emeralds |
| Potion of Night Vision | Blue | 2 | 75 emeralds |
| Potion of Fire Resistance | Yellow | 8 | 50 emeralds |

a) What is the difference in value between the Potion of Night Vision and the Potion of Healing?  ☐ emeralds

b) How many more bottles of Potion of Fire Resistance have been made than Potion of Leaping?  ☐ bottles

c) How many different colours of potion have been crafted by Oscar and Maya?  ☐ colours

d) What colour is the potion with greatest value? .................................

**2**

 This table shows the number of emeralds Oscar and Maya spent over five days.

| Day | 1 | 2 | 3 | 4 | 5 |
|---|---|---|---|---|---|
| Oscar | 12 | 15 | | 21 | 17 |
| Maya | 20 | 17 | 24 | | |

Complete the table using this information:
- Oscar spent half as many emeralds as Maya on day 3.
- On day 4, they spent a total of 34 emeralds.
- In total, Maya spent 93 emeralds across the five days.

**COLOUR IN HOW MANY EMERALDS YOU EARNED**

88

# ADVENTURE ROUND-UP

## NEW THINGS FROM THE NETHER

Maya has learned a lot from her journey into the Nether. Not only are the mobs much tougher, but it offers the chance to find new items to bring home and experiment with.

## SPECIAL SUPPER

Before bed, Maya treats herself to some pumpkin pie and milk. As she drinks the milk, she realises something – milk cures Poison and Bad Omen effects; does it cure Wither effect too? This is something she will try soon. For now, it's time for bed and dreams of even more exciting missions.

# ANSWERS

::::::::::::::::::::::::::::::::::::::::::::::::::::::::::::::::::::::::::::::::::::::::::::::::::::::::

## Page 5

1  400; 500; 700                                    [1 emerald]
2  a) 300 + 70 + 2                                   [1 emerald]
   b) 200 + 30 + 6                                   [1 emerald]
   c) 600 + 40 + 5                                   [1 emerald]
   d) 800 + 90 + 0                                   [1 emerald]
3  Any suitable answers. For example:
   a) 500 + 70 + 6       570 + 6                     [1 emerald]
   b) 800 + 70 + 3       870 + 3                     [1 emerald]
   c) 900 + 80 + 7       980 + 7                     [1 emerald]

## Pages 6–7

1  a) 37            b) 125
   c) 250           d) 302          [1 emerald each]
2  a)

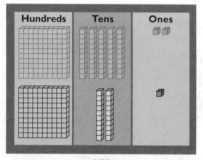

273                                                 [1 emerald]
   b)

458                                                 [1 emerald]
3  a) 127           b) 471          [1 emerald each]
4  a) 120           b) 150
   c) 190           d) 610
   e) 630           f) 680          [1 emerald each]
5  Accept suitable answers:
   a) From 22–28                                     [1 emerald]
   b) From 42–48                                     [1 emerald]
   c) From 80–86                                     [1 emerald]

## Pages 8–9

1  a) 65            b) 316          [1 emerald each]
2  a) Three hundred and seventy-nine    [1 emerald]
   b) Seven hundred and eighty-three    [1 emerald]
3  a) 246 Two hundred and forty-six     [1 emerald]
   b) 394 Three hundred and ninety-four [1 emerald]
4  a) 962 Nine hundred and sixty-two    [1 emerald]

   b) 321 Three hundred and twenty-one  [1 emerald]
   c) 976 Nine hundred and seventy-six  [1 emerald]
5  a) 349 Three hundred and forty-nine  [1 emerald]
   b) 258 Two hundred and fifty-eight   [1 emerald]
   c) 347 Three hundred and forty-seven [1 emerald]

## Pages 10–11

1  a) i)  28   228     ii) 587  787    [1 emerald each]
   b) i)  307  327     ii) 399  419    [1 emerald each]
2

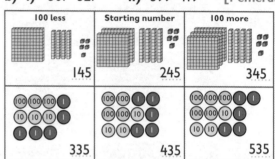

[1 emerald for each completed cell]
3

[1 emerald for each completed cell]
4  a) Always        b) Sometimes
   c) Never         d) Sometimes     [1 emerald each]

## Pages 12–13

1  a) 12; 16                                         [1 emerald]
   b) 16; 24; 40                                     [1 emerald]
   c) 100; 150; 300                                  [1 emerald]
   d) 200; 300; 400; 600                             [1 emerald]
2  a) 8       b) 50       c) 4        [1 emerald each]
3

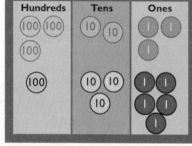

[1 emerald for each]
4  a) 24; 32       b) 48; 64       c) 850; 950
   d) 24; 16       e) 64; 48       [1 emerald each]
5  Any suitable answers. For example:
   a) 100          b) 200
   c) 200          d) 100          [1 emerald each]

## Pages 14–15

1  a) 101, 115, 122, 130, 146            [1 emerald]
   b) 226, 252, 263, 275, 277           [1 emerald]
   c) 36, 46, 48, 57, 69                    [1 emerald]
   d) 366, 368, 370, 374, 379           [1 emerald]
2  a) Any answer from 57–63 inclusive.     [1 emerald]
   b) Any answer from 129–133 inclusive.   [1 emerald]
   c) Any answer from 376–381 inclusive.   [1 emerald]
   d) Any answer from 413–432 inclusive.   [1 emerald]
3  a) <          b) >
   c) =          d) <          [1 emerald each]
4  368, 386, 638, 683, 836, 863
          [1 emerald for the numbers; 1 emerald for the order]
5  a) Any multiple of 10, up to 70        [1 emerald]
   b) 8 or 9                                 [1 emerald]
   c) 80; 100                                [1 emerald]
   d) <                                      [1 emerald]

## Page 16

1  a) Cart A: 422   Cart B: 394
      Cart C: 189   Cart D: 447     [1 emerald each]
   b) 189, 394, 422, 447            [1 emerald]
2  286                               [1 emerald]
3  Grid completed from top left to bottom right:
   16; 24; 40; 100; 200; 400 [1 emerald for each 3 correct]

## Page 19

1  a) $(10 + 80) + (4 + 5) = 90 + 9 = 99$     [1 emerald]
   b) $(400 + 500) + (80 + 0) + (4 + 2)$
      $= 900 + 80 + 6 = 986$          [1 emerald]
2  a) 39          b) 46          [1 emerald each]

## Pages 20–21

1  a) 89          b) 95
   c) 108         d) 58          [1 emerald each]
2  a) 928         b) 897
   c) 899         d) 719         [1 emerald each]
3  a) 84          b) 95
   c) 145         d) 117
   e) 114         f) 141         [1 emerald each]
4  a) 792         b) 876
   c) 860         d) 608
   e) 611         f) 981         [1 emerald each]
5  a) $448 + 211 = 659$          [1 emerald]
   b) $532 + 259 = 791$          [1 emerald]
   c) $327 + 437 = 764$          [1 emerald]
   d) $607 + 298 = 905$          [1 emerald]

## Pages 22–23

1  a) 84          b) 42
   c) 56          d) 41          [1 emerald each]
2  a) 434         b) 113
   c) 151         d) 141         [1 emerald each]
3  a) 35          b) 77

c) 18          d) 35
e) 15          f) 38          [1 emerald each]
4  a) 634         b) 206
   c) 181         d) 338
   e) 12          f) 92          [1 emerald each]
5  a) $55 - 44 = 11$              [1 emerald]
   b) $84 - 42 = 42$              [1 emerald]
   c) $634 - 230 = 404$           [1 emerald]
   d) $579 - 242 = 337$           [1 emerald]

## Pages 24–25

1  a) 100          b) 4
   c) 780          d) 50          [1 emerald each]
2  a) $300 + 200 = 500$           [1 emerald]
   b) $660 - 560 = 100$           [1 emerald]
   c) $60 \div 5 = 12$            [1 emerald]
   d) $12 \times 10 = 120$        [1 emerald]
3  a) 20      b) 50      c) 75      [1 emerald each]
4  a) $121 - 63 = 58$ or $121 - 58 = 63$   [1 emerald]
   b) $128 + 129 = 257$           [1 emerald]
   c) $15 \times 10 = 150$        [1 emerald]
   d) $28 \div 2 = 14$            [1 emerald]
5  a) Any suitable estimate, calculated answer of 998
      and inverse operation        [3 emeralds]
   b) Any suitable estimate, calculated answer of 442
      and inverse operation        [3 emeralds]

## Page 26

1  Oscar is wrong; he has 90 more points    [1 emerald]
2  a) Any suitable estimate, calculated answer of 932
      and inverse operation        [3 emeralds]
   b) Any suitable estimate, calculated answer of 73
      and inverse operation        [3 emeralds]

## Page 29

1  a) $8 \times 4 = 32$, $4 \times 8 = 32$, $32 \div 4 = 8$, $32 \div 8 = 4$
                                     [1 emerald each]
   b) $7 \times 3 = 21$, $3 \times 7 = 21$, $21 \div 3 = 7$, $21 \div 7 = 3$
                                     [1 emerald each]
2  a) 80          b) 8
   c) 210         d) 7            [1 emerald each]

## Pages 30–31

1  Numbers joined as follows: 8 to 16; 12 to 24;
   20 to 40; 25 to 50; 35 to 70; 60 to 120  [1 emerald each]
2  a) 48          b) 7
   c) 90          d) 70           [1 emerald each]
3  a) fifteen      b) nine
   c) eighty-eight  d) forty        [1 emerald each]
4  a) 8; 4; 2      b) 12; 6; 3
   c) 16; 8; 4     d) 20; 10; 5    [1 emerald each]
5  a) 100; 200     b) 40; 80       [1 emerald each]

## Pages 32–33

**1**

|   | ×1 | ×2 | ×3 | ×4 | ×5 | ×6 | ×7 | ×8 | ×9 | ×10 | ×11 | ×12 |
|---|----|----|----|----|----|----|----|----|----|-----|-----|-----|
| 3 | 3  | 6  | 9  | 12 | 15 | 18 | 21 | 24 | 27 | 30  | 33  | 36  |
| 4 | 4  | 8  | 12 | 16 | 20 | 24 | 28 | 32 | 36 | 40  | 44  | 48  |

[I emerald for each correct row]

**2 a)** 7 × 4 = 28, 4 × 7 = 28 [I emerald]
**b)** 9 × 3 = 27, 3 × 9 = 27 [I emerald]
**c)** 6 × 3 = 18, 3 × 6 = 18 [I emerald]
**d)** 3 × 5 = 15, 5 × 3 = 15 [I emerald]
**3 a)** 32 ÷ 4 = 8 **b)** 12 ÷ 3 = 4
**c)** 36 ÷ 12 = 3 [I emerald each]
**4 a)** 28 **b)** 8 **c)** 9 [I emerald each]
**5** 7 × 3 = 21, 3 × 7 = 21, 21 ÷ 7 = 3, 21 ÷ 3 = 7
[I emerald each]

## Pages 34–35

**1**

|   | ×1 | ×2 | ×3 | ×4 | ×5 | ×6 | ×7 | ×8 | ×9 | ×10 | ×11 | ×12 |
|---|----|----|----|----|----|----|----|----|----|-----|-----|-----|
| 8 | 8  | 16 | 24 | 32 | 40 | 48 | 56 | 64 | 72 | 80  | 88  | 96  |

[I emerald]

**2 a)**

| 40 | | | | |
|---|---|---|---|---|
| 8 | 8 | 8 | 8 | 8 |

[I emerald]

**b)**

| 80 | | | | | | | | | |
|---|---|---|---|---|---|---|---|---|---|
| 8 | 8 | 8 | 8 | 8 | 8 | 8 | 8 | 8 | 8 |

[I emerald]

**c)**

| 64 | | | | | | | |
|---|---|---|---|---|---|---|---|
| 8 | 8 | 8 | 8 | 8 | 8 | 8 | 8 |

[I emerald]

**3 a)** 40 ÷ 5 = 8 **b)** 32 ÷ 4 = 8
**c)** 32 ÷ 8 = 4 [I emerald each]
**4 a)** 8 × 3 = 24, 3 × 8 = 24 [I emerald]
**b)** 7 × 8 = 56, 8 × 7 = 56 [I emerald]
**c)** 6 × 8 = 48, 8 × 6 = 48 [I emerald]
**5 a)** 48 ÷ 8 = 6 **b)** 56 ÷ 7 = 8
**c)** 72 ÷ 8 = 9 **d)** 32 ÷ 4 = 8 [I emerald each]

## Pages 36–37

**1** Boxes joined as follows:
16 × 5  8 × 2 × 5  8 × 10 = **80** [I emerald]
3 × 40  3 × 4 × 10  12 × 10 = **120** [I emerald]
14 × 4  7 × 2 × 4  7 × 8 = **56** [I emerald]
16 × 4  16 × 2 × 2  32 × 2 = **64** [I emerald]
**2 a)** 11 × 3 × 2 = **33** × 2 = **66** [I emerald]
**b)** 20 × 4 × 2 = **80** × 2 = **160** [I emerald]
**c)** 12 × 3 × 2 = **36** × 2 = **72** [I emerald]
**d)** 7 × 3 × 10 = **21** × 10 = **210** [I emerald]
**3** Any suitable answers. For example:
**a)** 5 × 12 × 3 = **60** × 3 = **180** [I emerald]
**b)** 9 × 3 × 2 = **27** × 2 = **54** [I emerald]
**c)** 32 × 5 × 2 = 32 × **10** = **320** [I emerald]
**4 a)** 240; 240 [I emerald]
**b)** 80; 8 [I emerald]
**c)** 600; 600 [I emerald]
**5** 540 [I emerald]
180 × 3 = 540; 3 × 180 = 540;
540 ÷ 180 = 3; 540 ÷ 3 = 180 [I emerald]

## Pages 38–39

**1 a)** 20 × 4 + 9 × 4 = 80 + 36 = 116 [I emerald]
**b)** 30 × 8 + 6 × 8 = 240 + 48 = 288 [I emerald]
**c)** 40 × 3 + 6 × 3 = 120 + 18 = 138 [I emerald]
**d)** 30 × 5 + 1 × 5 = 150 + 5 = 155 [I emerald]
**2 a)** 28 × 3 = 84

| × | 20 | 8 |
|---|----|---|
| 3 | 60 | 24 |

[I emerald]

**b)** 24 × 8 = 192

| × | 20 | 4 |
|---|----|---|
| 8 | 160 | 32 |

[I emerald]

**c)** 26 × 4 = 104

| × | 20 | 6 |
|---|----|---|
| 4 | 80 | 24 |

[I emerald]

**3 a)** 192 **b)** 69
**c)** 296 **d)** 124 [I emerald each]
**4 a)** 152 **b)** 174 **c)** 108 [I emerald each]

## Pages 40–41

**1 a)**

| Tens | Ones |
|------|------|
| 10 10 | 1 |
| 10 10 | 1 |
| 10 10 | 1 |

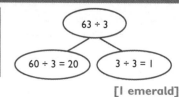

[I emerald]

63 ÷ 3 = 21 [I emerald]

**b)**

| Tens | Ones |
|------|------|
| 10 10 | 1 |
| 10 10 | 1 |
| 10 10 | 1 |
| 10 10 | 1 |

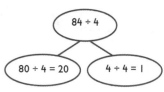

[I emerald]

84 ÷ 4 = 21 [I emerald]

**2 a)**

| Tens | Ones |
|------|------|
| 10 | 1 1 1 1 1 1 1 |
| 10 | 1 1 1 1 1 1 1 |
| 10 | 1 1 1 1 1 1 1 |

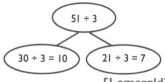

[I emerald]

51 ÷ 3 = 17 [I emerald]

**b)**

| Tens | Ones |
|------|------|
| 10 | 1 1 1 1 1 1 1 |
| 10 | 1 1 1 1 1 1 1 |
| 10 | 1 1 1 1 1 1 1 |
| 10 | 1 1 1 1 1 1 1 |

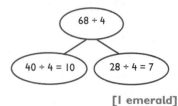

[I emerald]

68 ÷ 4 = 17 [I emerald]

**3 a)** 17 **b)** 19 **c)** 15 **d)** 19 [I emerald each]

## Page 42

**1 a)** Oscar: 4  Maya: 9  Jacob: 5  Cali: 6
[I emerald]
**b)** 24 **c)** 3 **d)** 6 [I emerald each]
**2** 72 [I emerald]
**3 a)** 14 **b)** 23 **c)** 12 [I emerald each]

## Page 45

1  a) Any 3 blocks coloured red, any 2 coloured yellow,
    any 1 coloured blue and any 4 coloured grey.
                                                [1 emerald]

   b)  $\frac{4}{10}$                           [1 emerald]

2  $\frac{2}{10}$    $\frac{4}{10}$    $\frac{7}{10}$    $\frac{8}{10}$    [1 emerald]

3  a)  3 villagers       b)  10 flowers
   c)  $\frac{3}{10}$ of a pumpkin   d)  $\frac{7}{10}$ of a cake  [1 emerald each]

## Pages 46–47

1  a)  $\frac{1}{5}$                 b)  $\frac{1}{3}$         [1 emerald each]
2  a)  $\frac{5}{8}$                 b)  $\frac{3}{8}$         [1 emerald each]
3  a)  $\frac{3}{7}$                 b)  $\frac{4}{9}$         [1 emerald each]
4  $\frac{3}{4}$   $\frac{6}{4}$ (or $1\frac{1}{2}$)   $\frac{7}{4}$ (or $1\frac{3}{4}$)  [1 emerald each]
5  Spruce: 6   Oak: 3   Birch: 3                    [1 emerald each]

## Pages 48–49

1  a)                              b)

          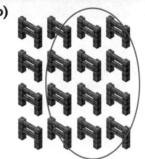

                                                [1 emerald each]
   c)  4; 12                                   [1 emerald]
2  a)  3 orange tulips    b)  2 cornflowers
   c)  4 lilacs                               [1 emerald each]
3  2                                           [1 emerald]
4  a)  18 sheep          b)  8 cows
   c)  27 chickens       d)  8 pigs            [1 emerald each]
5  a)  >                 b)  <
   c)  <                 d)  =                 [1 emerald each]

## Pages 50–51

1  a)  Any suitable shading leading to an answer of $\frac{4}{6}$
                                                [1 emerald]
   b)  Any suitable shading leading to an answer of $\frac{3}{4}$
                                                [1 emerald]
2  a)  $\frac{5}{6}$              b)  $\frac{4}{8}$ (or $\frac{1}{2}$)
   c)  $\frac{1}{9}$                           [1 emerald each]
3  a)  $\frac{5}{7}$              b)  $\frac{3}{14}$         [1 emerald each]
4  a)  $\frac{5}{14}$             b)  $\frac{7}{14}$ (or $\frac{1}{2}$)
   c)  $\frac{4}{14}$ (or $\frac{2}{7}$)                   [1 emerald each]
5  a)  $\frac{4}{8}$ (or $\frac{1}{2}$)    b)  $\frac{7}{8}$    [1 emerald each]

## Pages 52–53

1  a)  $\frac{1}{2}=\frac{2}{4}=\frac{3}{6}=\frac{4}{8}$  b)  $\frac{1}{3}=\frac{2}{6}=\frac{3}{9}$    [1 emerald each]
2  a)  2 sections shaded: $\frac{2}{4}$              [1 emerald]
   b)  4 sections shaded: $\frac{4}{8}$              [1 emerald]
   c)  3 sections shaded: $\frac{3}{6}$              [1 emerald]
   d)  5 sections shaded: $\frac{5}{10}$             [1 emerald]

3  a)  $\frac{1}{2}=\frac{2}{4}=\frac{4}{8}$               [1 emerald]
       $\frac{1}{3}=\frac{2}{6}=\frac{4}{12}$              [1 emerald]
       $\frac{2}{5}=\frac{4}{10}=\frac{8}{20}$             [1 emerald]
   b)  $\frac{16}{20}=\frac{8}{10}=\frac{4}{5}$            [1 emerald]
       $\frac{8}{12}=\frac{4}{6}=\frac{2}{3}$              [1 emerald]
       $\frac{40}{100}=\frac{20}{50}=\frac{10}{25}$        [1 emerald]
4  a)  $\frac{1}{5}=\frac{3}{15}=\frac{6}{30}$             [1 emerald]
   b)  $\frac{2}{3}=\frac{6}{9}=\frac{12}{18}$             [1 emerald]
   c)  $\frac{2}{4}=\frac{8}{16}=\frac{16}{32}$            [1 emerald]

## Pages 54–55

1  a)  Any suitable shading with $\frac{3}{4}$ circled   [1 emerald]
   b)  Any suitable shading with $\frac{2}{3}$ circled   [1 emerald]
2  a)  Any suitable shading with answer <    [1 emerald]
   b)  Any suitable shading with answer <    [1 emerald]
   c)  Any suitable shading with answer >    [1 emerald]
   d)  Any suitable shading with answer =    [1 emerald]
3  $\frac{1}{6}$   $\frac{1}{5}$   $\frac{1}{4}$   $\frac{1}{3}$   $\frac{2}{3}$   $\frac{5}{6}$   [1 emerald]
4  Fractions written on number line in this order from
   the left: $\frac{1}{10}$   $\frac{1}{4}$   $\frac{1}{2}$   $\frac{3}{5}$   [1 emerald]
5  a) >    b) =    c) <    d) >   [1 emerald each]

## Page 56

1  a)  6                 b)  $\frac{7}{10}$    [1 emerald each]
2  a)  7                 b)  27                [1 emerald each]
3  a)  Maya is wrong. $\frac{1}{4}$ is a smaller fraction than $\frac{1}{3}$
       because the whole has been split into 4 equal
       parts rather than only 3.               [1 emerald]
   b)  $\frac{2}{6}$ (or $\frac{1}{3}$)    c)  4    [1 emerald each]

## Page 59

1  5 cm                                        [1 emerald]
2  375 g                                       [1 emerald]
3  a)  3 litres          b)  1,750 ml          [1 emerald each]

## Pages 60–61

1  a)  300 cm = 3 m; 1 km 500 m = 1,500 m;
       30 mm = 3 cm                            [1 emerald]
   b)  3,000 ml = 3 l; 500 ml = 0.5 l; 5,000 ml = 5 l;
       30,000 ml = 30 l                         [1 emerald]
   c)  3 kg = 3,000 g; 2 kg 500 g = 2,500 g;
       3 kg 500 g = 3,500 g; 2 kg 50 g = 2,050 g  [1 emerald]
2  a)  3 km   b)  2 kg   c)  5 l        [1 emerald each]
3  3 cm and 7 mm < 35 cm and 7 mm < 3 m and 7 cm
   < 317 cm                                     [1 emerald]
4  Masses from left are: 100 g; 8 kg; 2.5 kg; 900 g
                                                [1 emerald each]
   Ordered: 100 g; 900 g; 2.5 kg; 8 kg          [1 emerald]

## Pages 62–63

1  45 m (moving up and then to the right)      [1 emerald]
   Other distances calculated (46 m and 54 m)
                                                [1 emerald each]

**2** **a)** 3 kg and 630 g **b)** 7 l and 705 ml
**c)** 6 km and 815 m **d)** 1 km and 220 m
**e)** 5 kg and 550 g **f)** 1 cm and 2 mm
[1 emerald each]
**3** **a)** 2 km and 350 m [1 emerald]
**b)** 4 kg and 750 g [1 emerald]

## Pages 64–65

**1** **a)** £8 and 52p **b)** £5 and 30p
**c)** £14 and 55p **d)** £10 and 45p [1 emerald each]
**2** **a)** £7 and 52p **b)** £14 and 93p
**c)** £12 and 44p **d)** £19 and 87p [1 emerald each]
**3** **a)** £19 and 31p **b)** £1 and 39p
**c)** £2 and 12p **d)** £6 and 19p [1 emerald each]
**4** **a)** £9 and 22p **b)** 78p [1 emerald each]

## Pages 66–67

**1** **a)** 10:10 Ten minutes past ten [1 emerald each]
**b)** 6:49 Eleven minutes to seven [1 emerald each]
**c)** 5:54 Six minutes to six [1 emerald each]
**d)** 8:17 Seventeen minutes past eight
[1 emerald each]

**2** **a)**  **b)**

**c)**  **d)**
[1 emerald each]

**3** **a)** Eight minutes past eight [1 emerald]
**b)** Twenty-eight minutes past two [1 emerald]
**4** **a)** 13 minutes past six in the evening 18:13 [1 emerald]
**b)**
04:45 [1 emerald]

## Pages 68–69

**1** **a)** April the third [1 emerald]
December the thirty-first [1 emerald]
June the first [1 emerald]
August the thirty-first [1 emerald]
**b)** April the third, June the first, August the thirty-first, December the thirty-first [1 emerald]
**2** **a)** 1,200 minutes **b)** 48 hours
**c)** 2 minutes **d)** 180 seconds
**e)** 3 weeks **f)** 10 hours [1 emerald each]
**3** **a)** March 25th [1 emerald]
**b)** Five times [1 emerald]
**c)** Monday, March 15th [1 emerald]
**4** **a)** > **b)** < **c)** > **d)** < [1 emerald each]

## Pages 70–71

**1** **a)** 1 hour (or 60 minutes) [1 emerald]
**b)** 1 hour and 15 minutes [1 emerald]
**c)** 1 hour and 30 minutes [1 emerald]
**2** **a)** 3 hours and 45 minutes [1 emerald]
**b)** 2 hours and 30 minutes [1 emerald]
**c)** 14 hours and 30 minutes [1 emerald]
**3** The game ends at the later time [1 emerald]
**4** **a)** 1:20 pm **b)** 11:55 am
**c)** 2:45 pm **d)** 5:29 pm [1 emerald each]
**5** 3:50 pm [1 emerald]

## Page 72

**1** **a)** 16 cm **b)** 20 cm [1 emerald each]
**2** **a)** 6 cm **b)** 10 cm
**c)** 6 cm **d)** 8 cm [1 emerald each]

## Page 75

**1** **a)** East **b)** South
**c)** West **d)** West [1 emerald each]
**2** **a)** 1; 3 **b)** 3; 1 [1 emerald each]
**3** fd2, lt90, fd1, rt90, fd2, rt90, fd3, lt90, fd3
[1 emerald for every three correct instructions]

## Pages 76–77

**1** Acute: B, D, F [1 emerald]
Right: E [1 emerald]
Obtuse: A, C [1 emerald]
**2** B < D < F < E < A < C [1 emerald]
**3**
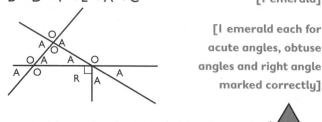
[1 emerald each for acute angles, obtuse angles and right angle marked correctly]

**4**

| I have four right angles. |
| I have two acute and two obtuse angles. |
| All my angles are obtuse. |
| All my angles are acute. |

[1 emerald each]

## Pages 78–79

**1**
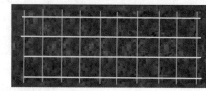
[1 emerald each for horizontal and vertical lines drawn]
**2** **a)** Vertical [1 emerald]
**b)** Horizontal and vertical [1 emerald]
**c)** Vertical [1 emerald]

**d)** Horizontal      [1 emerald]
**e)** Vertical      [1 emerald]
**f)** Horizontal and vertical      [1 emerald]
**3** Any two pairs of parallel lines identified   [1 emerald]
Any two pairs of perpendicular lines identified

     [1 emerald]
**4 a)** GH, CD or EF    **b)** CB or AH
   **c)** AB, EF or GH    **d)** BC or DE   [1 emerald each]

## Pages 80–81

**1** Any suitably coloured sword and matching key
     [1 emerald for each shape]
**2 a)** 32      **b)** 30
   **c)** 48      **d)** 45     [1 emerald each]
**3 a)** 5; 1               [1 emerald]
   **b)** 1; 2; 2           [1 emerald]
   **c)** 0; 1            [1 emerald]
**4**

| I have two pairs of parallel sides and two lines of symmetry. |
| I have four equal sides and two lines of symmetry. |
| I have two pairs of parallel sides and no lines of symmetry. |
| I have one pair of parallel sides. |

     [1 emerald each]

## Pages 82–83

**1 a)**

Vertex
Edge
Face

     [1 emerald]
**b)** 6; 12; 8      [1 emerald each]
**2**

| | Even number of vertices | Odd number of vertices | No vertices |
|---|---|---|---|
| Prism | A, C | | E |
| Not a prism | | B, D, F | |

     [1 emerald each]
**3**

| | Shape A | Shape B | Shape C | Shape D |
|---|---|---|---|---|
| Name of 3-D shape | Triangular-based pyramid (or tetrahedron) | Pentagonal prism | Cuboid | Square-based pyramid |
| Prism or pyramid? | Pyramid | Prism | Prism | Pyramid |
| Number of vertices | 4 | 10 | 8 | 5 |
| Number of faces | 4 | 7 | 6 | 5 |
| Number of edges | 6 | 15 | 12 | 8 |

     [1 emerald for each column]
**4 a)** Triangular prism    **b)** Cone   [1 emerald each]

## Pages 84–85

**1 a)** 2      **b)** 4      [1 emerald each]
   **c)** 1 and a half circles shown for Day 6   [1 emerald]
   **d)** 3 and a half circles shown for Day 7   [1 emerald]
   **e)** 12      [1 emerald]
**2**

| Day | 1 | 2 | 3 | 4 | 5 | 6 | 7 |
|---|---|---|---|---|---|---|---|
| Mobs seen | 6 | 9 | 5 | 7 | 8 | 3 | 7 |

[2 emeralds for all correct; 1 emerald for at least 4 correct]
**3** Pictogram completed as follows:
Plot A: 6 full circles      [1 emerald]
Plot B: 7 and a half circles      [1 emerald]
Plot C: 9 full circles      [1 emerald]
Plot D: 3 full circles      [1 emerald]
Plot E: 4 and a half circles      [1 emerald]
**4 a)** D      **b)** 6
   **c)** 3      **d)** 60     [1 emerald each]

## Pages 86–87

**1 a)** Flower     **b)** 10     [1 emerald each]
   **c)** Bar for melon drawn to 10 on the chart
     [1 emerald]
   **d)** 100      [1 emerald]
**2**

| Item | Chest | Wheat | Flower | Cobblestone | Melon |
|---|---|---|---|---|---|
| Number of items | 20 | 25 | 30 | 15 | 10 |

[2 emeralds for all correct; 1 emerald for at least 3 correct]
**3** Pictogram completed as follows:
Chest: 2 full circles      [1 emerald]
Wheat: 2 and a half circles      [1 emerald]
Flower: 3 full circles      [1 emerald]
Cobblestone: 1 and half circles      [1 emerald]
Melon: 1 full circle      [1 emerald]
**4 a)** 20      [1 emerald]
   **b)**

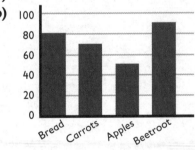

     [1 emerald for each bar]

## Page 88

**1 a)** 35 emeralds      [1 emerald]
   **b)** 2 bottles      [1 emerald]
   **c)** 4 colours      [1 emerald]
   **d)** Blue      [1 emerald]
**2** Table completed as follows:
Oscar, day 3:    12      [1 emerald]
Maya, day 4:    13      [1 emerald]
Maya, day 5:    19      [1 emerald]

# TRADE IN YOUR EMERALDS!

Well done for helping Oscar and Maya to make their adventures such a success! Along the way, you earned emeralds for your hard work. This merchant is waiting for you to spend your gems with them. Pretend you're preparing for an adventure of your own. Which items would you like to take with you?

If you have enough emeralds, you could buy more than one of some items.

Write the total number of emeralds you earned in this box:

HMMM?

## SHOP INVENTORY

- DIAMOND CHESTPLATE: 30 EMERALDS
- DIAMOND HELMET: 20 EMERALDS
- DIAMOND BOOTS: 20 EMERALDS
- DIAMOND SWORD: 25 EMERALDS
- NETHERITE PICKAXE: 30 EMERALDS
- NETHERITE SWORD: 35 EMERALDS
- ARROWS OF POISON: 15 EMERALDS
- ARROWS OF HEALING: 15 EMERALDS
- ENCHANTED BOOK: 15 EMERALDS
- GOLDEN APPLE: 10 EMERALDS
- GOLDEN CARROT: 15 EMERALDS
- COOKED PORKCHOP: 5 EMERALDS
- POTION OF REGENERATION: 30 EMERALDS
- POTION OF LEVITATION: 25 EMERALDS
- POTION OF INVISIBILITY: 35 EMERALDS

That's a lot of emeralds. Well done! Remember, just like real money, you don't need to spend it all. Sometimes it's good to save up.